THADDEUS LOWE: *Uncle Sam's First Airman*

The story of the daring young balloonist who organized an Aeronautics Corps for the Union army, conducted countless aerial reconnaissances, became "the most shot-at man in the Civil War," and saved the Army of the Potomac from destruction at Fair Oaks. Lowe flew a distance of nine hundred miles in a balloon he himself constructed and during the course of the Civil War he built up a fleet of observation balloons that served in many engagements. An inventor as well, Thaddeus Lowe was responsible for a machine for making ice and he equipped a steamer with refrigeration for hauling perishable foods.

Lydel Sims tells this interesting story with skill and verve.

Thaddeus Lowe:

Uncle Sam's First Airman

By Lydel Sims

G. P. Putnam's Sons • *New York*

For Mary and Pat

CONTENTS

CONTENTS

THADDEUS LOWE: *Uncle Sam's First Airman*

1

WEIRD LIGHT OVER
HINGHAM CENTER

THE night was black as axle grease. Across the bay a few pinpoints of light showed Boston was still up and stirring, but in Hingham Center most of the villagers had long since gone to bed. The few who were out late shivered a little in the strong wind blowing inland from the ocean a few miles away.

In the darkness a boy waited, jumping nervously at every sound.

Suddenly, as the wind died down, a soft whistle sounded behind him and he jerked around. Through the gloom a strange form was approaching, a creature that seemed to have four legs, a great squarish body, and two heads.

The boy gave a sigh of relief.

"There you are. What happened to you, Thad?"

The huge figure drew nearer, divided, and became two boys carrying a giant kite made of spruce and heavy paper.

"Nothing," said the taller of the newcomers. "It took a little longer than we thought, that's all. We didn't want anybody to see us. Where's William and the dog?"

"Didn't show up. I went to his house and he wouldn't even come out. Said he'd changed his mind."

"But what about the dog?"

"He said we couldn't use it. He's afraid something might happen to it."

Thad snorted in disgust, then held up his hand when one of his companions started to speak.

"Wait a minute. I think I have an idea." He stood silent a moment, scowling uneasily into the darkness. "Well, I don't like to do it," he said, "but I'll have to get Mr. Nash's cat. We've got to have an animal."

"But why, Thad? You might get into trouble."

"Why? To be sure it'll work right, that's why. If it does, I may build a bigger one and go up myself. Everybody tries animals first in these experiments."

There was another pause while he considered the problem.

"You two wait here," he said. "I have the keys to Mr. Nash's store. It won't take me a minute. Just don't let anybody see you."

He handed the kite over to the others and slipped away. Minutes passed but he did not return. The wind grew stronger. Somewhere a dog howled. Then a strange red patch of light appeared in the distance, moving toward them.

They looked at one another in alarm. As it drew nearer they withdrew into the shadows with the big kite.

"It's all right," a low voice called. "I've got the cat—and something else too!"

Thad was grinning proudly as he set down a wire cage holding a big black tomcat and thrust a slightly smaller object toward them. It was a watchman's lantern, with thin red tissue paper pasted over half the glass. Now that he removed the cloth that had partly covered it, the others could see that from one side it cast a clear, bright light; from the other, an eerie pink glow.

"Let's put on a real show," Thad whispered. "We'll send

up a cat *and* a lantern. That ought to give the people something to talk about!"

Silently, all three set to work. One took the big ball of strong cord attached to the kite and walked eastward along the dark street, heading directly into the wind and paying out the line until he was several hundred feet away. The others attached the tomcat's cage securely to the spruce framework near the lower end of the kite itself and then tied the lantern to the tail, about halfway down.

Thad called a soft warning down the street.

He and the other boy carefully raised the heavy kite as high as they could reach. Instantly it began pulling against the wind and the wire cage rocked violently. The cat arched its back and scratched frantically at the wire. As the boys steadied the kite the cage grew still.

The lantern sat upright in the street, the long kite tail trailing behind it. Thad moved rapidly. "All right, now, hang onto the kite . . . can you keep it steady by yourself? I'll guide the lantern up and then we'll both run to help hold the cord. Ready?"

"Ready."

Along the silent street went the hissed signal for action. "Let 'er go!"

It worked perfectly. At the moment the kite was released, the boy holding the cord gave a strong pull. The big craft instantly rose into the darkness, the lantern snaked out of Thad's hands, and he was running, running along the street, in a fever to help pay out the line.

"Hurry up! This thing's almost too strong for me!"

In another minute all three boys were hanging onto the line with all their strength, paying it out gradually as kite, cat and lantern rose majestically into the air over Hingham Center.

On and on it went, the line throbbing in the wind, the lantern spinning like a top.

"We're almost to the end. How much cord did you have, Thad?"

"About a thousand feet."

"*A thousand feet!* That old cat never thought it'd get that far off the ground!"

Fighting against the pull, they tied the end of the line to a hitching post and stood back, panting, to observe the results of their work.

Far above them and to the west a light blinked white and red, white and red as the lantern revolved steadily in the wind. Its rays occasionally caught the glimmer of the wire cage, but there was neither sight nor sound of the airborne tomcat. As the wind rose again the throbbing of the cord increased and grew to a penetrating ghostlike wail.

"What do we do now?"

Thad grinned triumphantly. "Suppose we go around to different parts of town and see how it looks."

"Fine. And maybe we can see what people think of it!"

It was a rewarding trip. For two hours the boys wandered about the village, admiring their work from every possible viewpoint, listening solemnly to the little knots of excited men who had gathered outdoors here and there to look at the strange light in the sky.

A man at the livery stable was sure it was a comet, and had his audience almost believing it. But a fat, bearded citizen outside the inn felt positive it was something else.

"It's a sign, gentlemen," he cried in a high nervous squeak. "Some kind of mystic sign for sure. I don't like it, I tell you!" As he scurried back into the inn the boys, hugging themselves with glee, returned to the hitching post where the kite was tied.

The line still throbbed loudly in the wind.

"This is going to be a real job. Let's get to work."

They wound cord in until their muscles ached. Slowly,

slowly the red and white light drew nearer. Then one of the boys cried in alarm.

"Look, is the kite on fire? I see something glowing up there."

Thad strained his eyes. Sure enough, not one but two bright points of light showed well above the tail of the kite. Then, as the big contraption came nearer, he laughed in relief.

"It's the cat's eyes!"

The frightened animal was standing stiff and unmoving in its cage, its eyes burning wildly in the night.

"Let's hurry, boys. That poor cat must be half frozen by now."

Another tug and the kite was down. Thad ran for the cage, beginning to feel guilty for the first time.

"It's all over now, boy. Everything's fine. I'm going to let you out and then I'll give you—"

As the door eased open, a furry black streak shot out and disappeared down the street. The flying tomcat had had enough.

The newspaper from Hingham, when it arrived next day, had a story about a mysterious changing light that had been observed over Hingham Center the night before by several reliable witnesses. In the firm of Nash, French and Company, makers of boots and shoes, Mr. Nash read the story thoughtfully, took another look at the unexplained fragments of tissue paper on the night watchman's lantern, and called for his apprentice.

"Thad, I wonder if you have any idea what could have happened to our cat. I haven't seen it all day."

"Cat?" Thad's face turned a fiery red under his thick black hair. "Why, Mr. Nash, I haven't seen that cat all day."

"No," said Mr. Nash ruefully, "I didn't think you had. Well, anyway we got our lantern back."

2

BOY WITH A DREAM

IT HAD worked, it had really worked! Thad let the exultation pound through him again as he returned to his bench. Anybody could make a kite, but it took planning and hard work to make one strong enough and airworthy enough to carry a living passenger . . . to take the fierce blows of the wind without breaking . . . to come down at last in perfect safety.

And that was only the beginning. Kites and cats were for practice.

Some day he would be the one in the basket, and towering above him as he flew free and triumphant through the air would be no wooden kite but a great balloon. And then, along with the names of such pioneers as the Montgolfiers, Jeffries, Blanchard, Wise and the others, the world would write his own.

His own name. Thad let his mind listen to the sound. Thaddeus Sobieski Constantine Lowe, aeronaut.

It was his mother's idea, that name. She had it all ready for him when he was born in the yellow frame house at Jefferson Mills sixteen years ago in the summer of 1832.

August 20 was his birthday. It would have been hot that day, the sun beating down on the rugged New Hampshire landscape, the White Mountains rising sharp and tall in the distance, trout jumping in the river a few rods from the house. And Alpha Green Lowe, her head filled with great names of history and romance, must have looked at her husband hopefully and said:

"Let's give him a special name, Clovis. Something to live up to."

She had given him more than a special name to live up to, Thad mused. His memories of her were already dim, for she had died when he was a small boy, but the dreams she had given him would be with him always. From his father he had learned a restless energy; it was his mother who had taken that energy and given it a goal—to learn about the world around him, to be interested in everything, to ask questions and seek the answers.

Her questions, her stories, the books she had read to him before he was old enough to read for himself, these were what had first set him wondering and dreaming. She had been interested in everything.

Buried treasure, even. She had been the first to tell him about the Rangers. Bending over his workbench, he smiled at a sudden memory . . .

"Come on, Thad! The cave's just at the foot of that bank. Come on!"

(He would have been—oh, maybe nine then. That was the year he got so excited about looking for the Lost Treasure of the Rangers.)

He and Samuel reached it together in a running, stumbling rush. It was a cave, all right, hidden from sight until you got right up on it, a fair-sized cave too from the look of it, with a passage turning off to the right.

Both boys slowed to a stop as they reached the entrance, suddenly a little doubtful about going in.

"You think this could be it, Thad?"

"I don't know." Parts of the story came pouring into his head. Major Robert Rogers, the daring Indian fighter, leading his famous Rangers from Lake Champlain up to the great fortress of the Abenakis Indians on the St. Lawrence . . . wiping out the village from which so many attacks on the English settlers had been mounted . . . discovering the fabulous treasures collected by the Indians . . . setting out for the return trip with his wounded and the spoils of war.

Could some of the treasures be in this cave?

"Well, let's look. What if we found the golden candlesticks?"

Thad grunted. "We won't find them. Don't you remember the story? Somebody found them before we were born, up around Lake Memphremagog. But there's plenty of other treasure that never turned up."

They ventured into the entrance, walking nervously on their toes. It was cold and damp in the narrow passageway. They reached the bend, pushed ahead eagerly—and came almost at once to a blank stone wall. Thad groaned.

"All this work, and nothing to show for it. Just another empty cave. Sometimes I wonder if there really is any treasure."

Outside again, they flung themselves down to rest and talk about the legends. How much was true? The Rogers Rangers had raided the Abenakis, there was no doubt about that. Even the schoolteacher had told the story Thad had first heard from his mother. Two hundred Indians had been killed, twenty women and children had been taken prisoners. The Rangers had found hundreds of English scalps waving from the lodge-poles of the wigwams.

And then? Well, the Rangers' provisions had given out on the way home, and they had divided the treasure and sepa-

rated into small parties. Few of them ever got back to Crown
Point on Lake Champlain. The others had starved or frozen
to death or died in Indian ambushes.

But the treasure? Had there really been a great treasure,
and was it hidden somewhere here around Israel's River as
the stories said? Thad didn't know. Maybe the treasure was
no more real than the screeching ghost of a starved Ranger
that people sometimes heard on windy nights.

Gradually their talk died down. Both boys felt tired and a
little drowsy in the hot afternoon after their long search.
Thad lay back against a tree and began looking upward
through its boughs at the sky.

Clouds were a funny thing. You'd expect them all to move
one way, but they didn't. Those low ones down over the
mountains were going west. But up higher were other clouds,
and they were moving toward the east.

Sleepily, he puzzled over the problem. Low-lying clouds
drifted wherever the changing winds blew them. But if they
were high enough, they always seemed to go in the same direction—eastward.

It was almost as if they were floating along a river. The
lower clouds were in eddies or backwaters, moving to and
fro. The higher ones . . .

"A river," he heard himself murmur. "A great river in the
sky."

Samuel stirred beside him. "A what? Thad, are you talking
in your sleep?"

Thad shook himself. Maybe he had been. They got up and
began the walk back to the river. But along the way he found
himself musing over a new thought that drove the Lost Treasure of the Rangers from his mind.

What would it be like to *sail* on that river in the sky?

He had wondered about it often during the hard, cold
New Hampshire winters. He loved winter, because it meant

a chance to go to school. During three whole months he could
leave off most of his farm chores and give his thoughts and
energies to books.

It was like taking a vacation. School was only two miles
across the river from home, just a good walk on snowshoes
through Stalbird Hollow and over Indian Hill. In the after-
noons, instead of fighting the roots and rocks on the farm, he
did chores at the Red Tavern in the village, helping about
the stable or bringing in wood for the fireplaces. It was light,
easy work and he enjoyed it. Besides, now and then a traveler
left interesting books or magazines behind him.

Once, in a dusty storeroom, he found an old copy of the
Southern Literary Messenger. Leafing through the yellowed
pages of the magazine he came upon a story by a writer
named Edgar Allan Poe. It was called "The Unparalleled
Adventure of One Hans Pfaall," and it told of an imaginary
balloon trip to the moon.

Thad had never cared much for fiction, but he lost himself
completely in the accounts of what it was like to fly. From
far up in the air, the author said, the earth had a concave
appearance. It looked like the inside of a bowl—just the
opposite of what you would expect. And when you got high
enough, you left weather behind you. You sailed above
the clouds in a quiet, peaceful world of your own.

At night as he walked home from the inn, Thad would
wonder about it. Then he would go out to the pile of pine
knots he had gathered in the fall, select a few of them, and
bring them in to the fire. He lounged by the fireplace for
hours, reading his school books by its light.

Science, mechanics, chemistry—those were the subjects he
liked to read about. And more and more he looked for anything he could find about man's age-old dream of flying
through the air in great ships.

There was a great deal to find, not only in his books but

in the newspapers as well, for all America was excited about balloons.

Men like Charles Durant, William Paullin and John Wise were going about the country making ascensions in the big cities. Richard Clayton had electrified the country by flying three hundred and fifty miles in a balloon from Cincinnati to somewhere in Virginia. Everywhere, Thad thought enviously, men were doing great things in the air. Thousands talked about their exploits. The newspapers were full of them.

One night just before his eleventh birthday, he read an announcement that filled him with fresh excitement. It was signed by John Wise, the famous aeronaut, and it announced that Wise was going to fly across the ocean. Thad's eyes raced over the bold words:

"As it is my intention to make a trip across the Atlantic Ocean with a balloon in the summer of 1844, and as the descent or landing of balloons, in my experience, has almost universally created unnecessary alarm and consternation in the people nearby, I therefore give this general notice to the sea-faring community, of all climes, that should they, during any time henceforth, chance to be in the vicinity of a balloon, either on the ocean or in the atmosphere, they need not be under any fearful apprehensions, but endeavor to give aid to its adventurers. . . ."

It was flowery and swaggering, but there was a sort of majesty about it. Thad read on feverishly.

The balloon would be one hundred feet in diameter, Wise said, with an ascending power of 25,000 pounds. Instead of the usual basket beneath, it would carry a seaworthy boat for use in case the balloon sank into the ocean.

He jumped up from his place by the fire and showed the announcement to his father.

"Do you think he really means it?"

Clovis Lowe scratched his chin. "I don't know," he said thoughtfully. "It sounds risky . . ."

"But a balloon has already crossed the English Channel! I read about it at school. There were two men in it. If the Channel can be crossed, why not the ocean?"

"There's a difference," his father said dryly.

But it could be done, Thad told himself stubbornly. Maybe not by John Wise, and maybe not next year. But some day. Maybe by Thaddeus S. C. Lowe!

He was thinking about it as he went to bed. Passing the room in which his stepmother was making a quilt, he stopped to say goodnight. Mary Randall Lowe paused in her work and smiled at him absently. Then, still intent on her work, she turned back to Moranda Hicks, a neighbor girl who had come in to help.

"We will not tack the quilt very closely," she said. "I may be obliged to take out the wool and spin it to clothe my children."

As he crawled into bed, Thad pondered her words. Money, he knew, was always a problem. Clovis Lowe was looked up to in the community—he had served as selectman and had been a delegate to the New Hampshire legislature—but he was not wealthy, and his family was large. While the farm and the cobbler shop provided food for all, there was little money for other necessities, let alone luxuries like new clothes and books.

And yet he was dreaming of a balloon big enough to cross the ocean! How would he ever get the education he would need? Or the money to travel, to experiment, to build his balloon? What was to happen to his dream?

The answer came sooner than he expected. One day his father called him out of the house.

"Let's take a walk, Thad," he said. "I want to talk to you."

Clovis Lowe was strangely uncomfortable. The time had come, he said, when Thad must go to work to support himself. There was a neighbor who would give him a home in exchange for his work. It had all been settled.

Such arrangements were common enough, Thad knew, but he was suddenly chilled to find it happening to him. He was ready to give up his long hours of hunting and fishing with the Indian boys on Indian Hill, but what about school? Were his days of learning behind him?

His father was talking on unhappily, trying to reassure him. It would simply be like joining another family, he said. Thad would be working for his keep like a grown man, but there would be hours he could call his own. And in a few years he could strike out for himself.

"And school?"

Clovis frowned uneasily. "I don't know, son. I just don't know. We'll have to wait and see."

So Thad went to work for a neighbor, and with every month the life grew more unbearable. The family was a kindly one, and the work was no harder than he had done at home, but it seemed to him that the mountains were closing in on him. He was growing up now, and he must begin working to make his dream come true or forget it. Forget it and settle down to be a farmer.

As he thought, a plan began to grow in his mind. . . .

He set out at night, without telling anybody.

He wasn't ashamed of what he was doing. But if he discussed it with anyone, even his father, he knew he might be persuaded to give up his plan.

"Not yet, Thad," he could hear Clovis Lowe protest. "A boy your age should stay home a while longer. What could you do in Boston? How would you get there? Don't you know that even Portland is a hundred miles away, and you'd have to take a ship from there? It's out of the question."

So, since it was out of the question, he had decided not to put the question in the first place.

Some way, he would get to Boston. He would walk every step of the way to Portland if necessary, and once there he would somehow get ship passage to Boston. He had saved a few dollars from his work at the Red Tavern. And in Boston he would seek out his older brother, Joseph, who lived there. Together they could find work for him that would leave him time to study.

And so he turned his back on the mountains and set out for a new life.

It was hard going even for Thad, tall and tough-muscled at fifteen, but in a way it was an adventure. There were occasional wagons along the turnpike to Portland, and now and then he was offered a ride. There were barns to sleep in along the way, and fish waiting to be caught when he slept out in the open. Almost before he knew it he was at Portland, making a bargain with the master of a sailing ship who was glad to pick up a few extra dollars from a boy willing to sleep on deck.

Boston, when he reached it, was bigger than he could believe. As he searched for his brother, he began to wonder if he had made a mistake after all. Could he ever find a place in this busy, teeming city?

Joseph's scowl, when Thad found him, renewed his doubts.

"You shouldn't have done it, Thad. My goodness, do you have any idea . . ." He shook his head darkly. Then, looking at his younger brother, he smiled and a gleam of sympathy came into his eyes.

"I know what it's like, Thad, and I suppose I can't blame you. Well, let me see what I can do. I know a fine man at Hingham Center, not far from here. Maybe he can use an apprentice."

They went to Nash, French and Company, and Joseph told Thad's story for him. Mr. Nash looked doubtfully at the tall, rawboned boy before his desk.

"That's all very well, but can you cut leather?"

Suddenly Thad grinned. His father had taught him a few tricks of shoemaking, and one of his Indian friends had passed on a secret few white men knew. "Let me try," he said.

Leather and a knife were brought. Thad turned his back to Mr. Nash and his brother and worked for a few minutes. Then he handed back the leather, cut now into the pattern that had been marked on it.

Mr. Nash examined it, raised an eyebrow, and turned to Joseph.

"I think this boy can be taught," he said. "And we will be glad to have him in our home, Joseph, and to give him time for the studies you say he is so eager to pursue."

Then he turned to Thad. "It will be hard work," he said sternly, though Thad thought he was hiding a smile. "You have much to learn, and I will expect you to earn your money. But we shall see."

So the apprenticeship had begun. It was not until a week later that Mr. Nash drew Thad aside and asked:

"Son, how do you manage to cut the leather so neatly? I didn't want to admit it that first day, but you are the best cutter I've ever had in my employ."

Grinning proudly, Thad told him the secret of the Indians —if you wet the cutting knife with saliva before you start, the leather can be cut more precisely.

Well, that had been a year ago, Thad told himself, bringing his mind back to the present. It had been a good year. Mr. Nash was a good man to work for. There had been plenty of time to study and experiment. . . .

There had even been a cat and a lantern handy last night when he needed them for his kite!

Remembering the night's adventure, Thad chuckled. Then his thoughts turned to the experiments he had planned for the future.

Licking them, he thought wryly, would not be as simple as licking a cutting knife.

3

PROFESSOR OF SOAP BUBBLES

THE little Professor walked briskly onto the stage and bowed to the audience. Turning to the velvet-draped table beside him, he indicated two glasses, one empty and the other filled with a colorless liquid.

With a flourish he lifted the empty glass and turned it upside down. Then he righted it, reached for the other glass, and paused dramatically.

"Observe how water may be changed into wine!"

As he poured the liquid from one glass to another, it seemed to turn as if by magic into a rich red wine. The Professor bowed again, drank the concoction, smacked his lips, and waited for the burst of applause to die down.

"And now," he said, "before we delve deeper into the wondrous realms of science, I wonder if I might have a volunteer from this fine New Hampshire audience?"

There was a moment's silence. Then a tall, dark-haired young man, his face unnaturally pale, rose and began making his way to the stage.

"There's your volunteer, Professor!" someone shouted.

"Thad can help you. He's been all the way to Boston and back. Tell him what you learned about science down there, Thad!"

Thaddeus Lowe turned to grin self-consciously, stumbled, regained his balance, and continued his way while his friends laughed, stamped their feet, and applauded.

At least it would be a change, he thought. And he needed something to take his mind off his problems. He was tired of worrying about the future.

He was feeling stronger now, but the illness that had ended his exciting life at Hingham Center had left him thin and nervous. It wasn't fair, he told himself. To have to leave the libraries and lectures of Boston just when his experiments were going so well!

But he had fallen gravely ill. Mr. Nash could not be expected to take care of him indefinitely. As soon as he was strong enough to travel, he had given up his apprenticeship and returned to the White Mountains to stay with his family.

They had been glad to see him, and through the lazy days his strength had begun to come back. It had been pleasant enough, especially the long talks with his father about Thad's studies in aeronautics. Clovis Lowe loved to listen and ask questions.

"I've been working too hard to keep up with the latest advances in science," he told his son. "You'll have to tell me everything you've learned." And Thad had been impressed by the ease with which his father grasped the principles of ballooning.

But where would it lead? He had lost his job. He was back home where he started, and time was passing. Suddenly the thought that he was almost eighteen seemed to stagger him. How would he ever find his way out of the mountains a second time and begin making his dream come true?

The Professor was beaming at him.

"Thank you, young man, thank you! I am sure you will be

of great assistance to us all. And now, if you will hold this beaker while I wave my wand . . ."

It was a good show the little "Professor of Chemistry" gave, though he was not a real professor and everybody knew it. The title was often used by traveling showmen. But for all that, his performance had its scientific side. First he would perform some amazing feat that ended with an explosion or a cloud of smoke or a disappearance, and then he would go back and explain the chemical laws responsible.

During the applause at the end of the show, the Professor drew Thad aside. "Young man, you have been a great help to me. It is not often that I find an assistant so quick to grasp what needs to be done. Would you like to come back for my performances tomorrow night, and the next?"

Thad smiled at the little man. "Why not?"

"Fine. Perhaps you would like some free tickets for your friends."

So for two nights more the magical demonstrations went on, and Thad found he was enjoying the fun more and more. When it was all over, the Professor spoke to him again.

"Now that we are better acquainted, Thaddeus, I would like to make you an offer. You are interested in these things I do, and you are a good assistant. Well, it is a good life. I travel about the country, living well, doing what I enjoy doing, happy in the thought that wherever I go I stir up the slumbering brain cells of those unfortunate victims of the humdrum drabness of . . ."

Thad tried to hold back a smile. When the Professor got wound up, he could really go! He listened as the phrases grew more and more flowery. Then the Professor checked himself.

"But enough of that. My point, young Thaddeus, is that I would like for you to accompany me on my meanderings as a salaried assistant. The salary will not be princely, but the hours will be easy and the opportunities for study many. And some day I may wish to sell my modest equipment to a worthy successor . . ."

Even before he talked it over with his father late that night, Thaddeus knew what his answer would be. He had found a way out of the mountains at last!

The next day, when the touring show set out for a new town, the Professor of Chemistry had a permanent assistant.

A loud explosion sounded offstage and a cloud of blue smoke poured in from the wings. Through it strode Professor Thaddeus S. C. Lowe, his eyes turned piercingly toward the audience, his mouth stern under an auburn mustache.

Even before he turned to the velvet-draped table in the center of the stage, the audience was applauding warmly. They were New Yorkers and not easily pleased, but they knew the reputation of Professor Lowe. It would be a good show.

Thad was twenty-two now, six feet tall, broad-shouldered and powerful. With the mustache, he knew, he could easily pass as a much older and more experienced man. And he knew his business.

As he had gone from city to city, first as an assistant and later as a Professor of Chemistry himself with a portable laboratory of his own, he had learned many things. He had a polish about him now that made him seem more like a French diplomat than a New Hampshire farm boy. He had picked up a flair for speaking, for doing everything in a dramatic fashion, for making friends with the newspaper reporters whose good will meant business success for him.

And he had gained other things even more important. He had bought new books, studied, visited aeronauts and men of science all through the country. And his bank account was growing. Soon now there would be enough money for him to set to work in earnest, building his own balloon!

Quickly he ran through a series of dramatic experiments

for his audience. Then, before the applause died, he raised a hand for silence.

"And now," he cried, "we return to an instructive matter that was of great interest to the alert citizens who attended last evening's lecture—the subject of soap bubbles!"

He made mysterious motions with his hands. Out into the bright glare of the footlights poured a flood of bubbles, floating upward toward the ceiling before they began to drift downward and disappear against the floor.

"The soap bubble!" said Professor Thaddeus Lowe in his most impressive voice. He paused, touched a hand to his mustache, and stared dreamily off into the distance.

"The soap bubble! An airy bauble, insubstantial, meaningless, useful only to entertain an infant bouncing on its mother's knee.

"But is it?" At the sudden change in his voice, at the sight of his piercing eyes, the audience stirred with excitement.

"No! It is more than that, far more. Ladies and gentlemen, how many of you are aware tonight of the vast importance of soap bubbles in scientific research? How many know the hours spent by men of learning in coaxing from these dainty orbs new secrets about color, light, and surface tension?"

The audience stirred again. Thaddeus noticed a small, bright face turned toward him from one of the nearest seats. If he had ever taken time to bother with girls, he thought, that was the sort of girl who would appeal to him. Dainty as a soap bubble herself!

"Last evening we considered the difference between a soap bubble and a raindrop, and the great importance of that difference. Together we watched the magic play of colors about the surface of the lovely soap bubble, and together we sought the cause of this iridescence.

"We talked of reflection and refraction and interference, and I make bold to suggest that we emerged from these studies with a better understanding of the world about us. . . ."

He was getting more and more like the old Professor every day, he told himself. Windier and windier! Was the pretty girl actually hiding a yawn? He would have to do better.

"Last night's bubbles sank, every one, to the floor. Delicate as they are, they are heavier than air. Tonight I have promised to reverse that situation. Let us break the law of gravity, friends. Behold!"

Again he turned to the table. A fresh cascade of bubbles burst forth, drifted upward—and, instead of falling back, continued to climb.

Up and up they went until they lodged against the ceiling itself. The audience burst into fresh applause.

Thaddeus allowed himself a quick sigh of relief. The talk was important—you had to impress them with what you were about to do—but for a minute there he had been afraid he had overdone it.

He stole a look at the pretty girl near the front. She was gazing upward as happily as the others.

"And now, my friends," he continued as the sea of faces turned back to the stage, "I have a confession to make—one that the more learned members of our group will already have anticipated.

"We did not break the law of gravity tonight. None of us is able to do that. Instead, we worked within natural laws to give the appearance of the unnatural. Those bubbles are indeed soap bubbles, but they are filled not with air but with hydrogen, the lightest of all elements, lighter than air itself. And so the bubbles rose.

"Of what value, you ask, is this child's play? Of incalculable value! Translate that soap bubble into a balloon, my friends! Fill it with hydrogen! Venture yourself into the basket—and

you may sail out to explore and conquer the very heavens
themselves!"

After the show he had late supper in the dining room of
his New York hotel. He was leaving when he saw an acquaint-
ance in a group at another table. He had passed with a nod
when his eye caught another member of the party— the beautiful girl he had seen at the lecture.

Later, he was not sure why he turned back. He had had
little time for girls—and now, with his Mississippi River tour
little more than a week away, he had less time than ever. Certainly none to waste on a glamorous New Yorker who looked
as if she had never known the meaning of hard work.

But whatever the reason, he found himself stopping, going
back to the table, greeting his friend with unnecessary
warmth. And when the introductions were performed, he
heard only one of them.

". . . Mademoiselle Leontine Augustine Gachon, formerly
of Paris. . . ."

Suddenly the distinguished Professor Thaddeus S. C. Lowe
felt like just what he was, an embarrassed twenty-two-year-old
mountain boy unable to do anything but blush and stammer.

"But I have met him already, this very night, from the audience!" she was saying, in a voice that turned his knees to
water. "M'sieu, you were *magnifique!*"

"Uh . . . merci!" Thaddeus blurted, and had to wipe the
perspiration from his forehead.

Desperately he thanked his stars for remembering that one
French word. He had come within an ace of saying, "Aww,
shucks!"

For all her frail beauty, it developed, the tiny Mademoiselle
Leontine was no hothouse flower. At nineteen she had been
through trials that chilled Thad's blood as he learned of them.

Her father had been an officer in the royal guard of the

French "citizen-king," Louis Philippe. Early in 1848, when Leontine was still a young girl, Paris had been swept by revolt. The king was dethroned, the Second Republic set up, and Leontine and her parents barely got out of the city with their lives, fleeing through streets that ran with blood.

Leontine's father had brought them to America, found them a home among French friends in Hoboken, New Jersey, and returned to his troubled country. On his first night back in Paris he had been killed.

Left unprotected in a strange land, mother and daughter had been forced to make their own way. Madame Gachon launched a little business, manufacturing and selling a bleach and antiseptic whose formula she had brought from France. Leontine, when she grew older, had become a professional dancer.

"And a good one, M'sieu le Professeur," she told him, laughing, one night, a week after they had met. It was the first time she had spoken to him of her earlier life. Thaddeus had talked all the other nights—talked endlessly, it sometimes seemed to him after he had left her, about his plans, about life in the White Mountains, about anything that might keep her by his side a little longer.

"So good a dancer," he asked, feeling suddenly lightheaded, "that you would not wish to leave the stage?"

A smile twitched her lips. "Does the Professor perhaps have a suggestion in mind?"

Thaddeus blushed violently. She was teasing him, he could tell. She could lay on that French accent or leave it off at will. Well, he was a fool, but he would get the words spoken if it killed him.

"Miss Leontine," he said with a sort of calm despair, "I don't know how to play games. You know that any airs I have are only put on for my shows. But I know what I want."

"Oui?"

"I'm leaving in a few days for a tour down the Mississippi

River to give my lectures, and better than anything in the world I'd like to take you with me as my wife. Oh, I know you're laughing at me. I just wanted to—"

Mademoiselle Leontine put a small hand over his mouth. When she spoke, the French accent was gone.

"Thaddeus," she said gently, "I was beginning to think I would have to ask you myself."

4

AIRBORNE AT LAST

"BUT I do not understand. What will make your beautiful toy balloons go up into the air?"

Thaddeus ran his fingers through his black hair and smiled at the look of concentration on his wife's face. He turned back to the gaily colored tissue-paper forms on the floor and picked up one shaped like a cow.

"Here, I'll show you."

Carefully he began blowing into the cow's left rear foot. The paper expanded, bulged, and began to look more than ever like a cow. He blocked the hole and took the balloon to the little stove that warmed the room.

"Look, now, and tell me what you see."

Leontine watched as he held the paper cow over the hot stove. "It is . . . I believe . . . yes, it is getting bigger . . . and bigger and bigger. Thaddeus, be careful! After all your work, suppose it should tear?"

"Don't worry. That's why I coated the paper with linseed oil. Makes it stronger and more airtight. But you're right. It's getting bigger. Now, can you tell me why?"

His little French wife wrinkled her forehead in concentration. "Something you said at last night's lecture. Ah! Expan-
sion. The air is heated and expands?"

"Right again. And when air expands it gets lighter. And
when it expands so much that the balloon is lighter than air—
well, watch."

Gently he released the bulging cow. It floated up slowly,
rolling about in an undignified way, and came to rest against
the ceiling.

"Observe!" Thaddeus cried in his best lecture-platform
voice. "The cow is now prepared to jump over the moon!"

Leontine laughed and clapped her hands.

"First lesson," he went on in a normal voice. "To sail
through the air, man must have a ship that is lighter than air.
Your famous countrymen the Montgolfiers understood that
much at least."

"That much? Then what did they fail to understand?"

"A small thing, really. You know the Montgolfiers were
the fathers of aeronautics, and I do not mean to criticize.
Think of it, it all began less than seventy-five years ago with
their first fire balloon! They made a bag and filled it with
smoke from a fire under it and—"

"But you said they did not understand."

"About the smoke. They had seen smoke rise, and they
thought it had a lifting power of its own. It doesn't, of course.
It's just that the air in the balloon was hot. You see—"

"Look out, Thaddeus! The so beautiful cow!"

The balloon was settling gradually downward toward the
stove. Thaddeus grabbed for it.

"Lesson number two." He grinned easily. "When the air
cools off, the balloon loses altitude."

Leontine thought this over for a moment. Then she cried
out in alarm. "But you talk of going up in balloons yourself.
So! And what will happen when the hot air is no longer hot?"

Thaddeus roared with laughter. "But I will not use hot

air for myself. I will use coal gas or hydrogen. They are lighter than hot air, and they remain light. Let me try your arithmetic. One hundred cubic feet of air weighs—oh, about one hundred and twenty-eight ounces. But one hundred cubic feet of hydrogen weighs—let's see, nine ounces. So tell me, my little scientist, how much lifting power would I have per hundred cubic feet of hydrogen?"

"One subtracts the nine from the one hundred twenty-eight?"

"True, true."

"Then you would have . . . I know, one hundred nineteen ounces of lifting power."

"Exactly."

"But that is only a few pounds. Not nearly as much as you weigh."

"Then I must make a large balloon, eh? I will not go up hanging onto a little paper cow. I will make my balloon of the best silk, India tassore, with plenty of varnish on it to make it airtight, and I will build it big enough to hold thousands of cubic feet of hydrogen. The gas will escape only when I want it to—when I open a valve in the top."

Leontine made a face at him. "If you must, I suppose you must."

They were on their honeymoon trip along the Mississippi River, a honeymoon during which they talked more about balloons than about love. Every day Thaddeus was more impatient to have his own balloon, to give up lecturing and launch a new career in the sky. Every night they counted the proceeds from his lectures and added what they could to the balloon fund.

And, partly because the public loved them but mostly because they gave him a chance to experiment, Thaddeus was adding more and more balloons to his show.

The tissue papers on the floor of the inn room were a part of it. He used dozens of them. To some he attached small fireworks, so that after they arose in the lecture hall there would be a dramatic explosion or a flash of light. Leontine helped him paint the figures—strange lopsided men, wild animals, fishes, whatever struck their fancy.

And as they worked, Thaddeus found himself explaining in more and more detail the wonderful story of what man had done with balloons in less than a century.

It had begun with the Montgolfier brothers, Joseph and Étienne, and almost from the moment their fire balloon rose through the air Europe had been ablaze with enthusiasm.

Other fire balloons followed, but soon men guessed that a light gas would be better than hot air. A Professor Charles at the French Academy of Sciences made a hydrogen balloon and sent it up for a fifteen-mile flight that electrified Paris. Suddenly everyone was making balloons.

At first animals had been used as passengers. A sheep, a rooster and a duck all went up together in one flight. Then the bolder adventurers decided to try it themselves. By 1785, only two or three years after the first fire balloon, Pierre Blanchard and Dr. John Jeffries had actually sailed across the Channel from England to France. King Louis XVI himself received them at Versailles and did them honor.

As other daring flights continued in Europe, America awoke to the excitement. Benjamin Franklin wrote home from France about the wonderful new device. George Washington predicted that some day a balloon might even cross the ocean. Thomas Jefferson talked eagerly of its scientific and military possibilities.

But it remained for a thirteen-year-old boy to be the first to ascend in America.

It was a small Montgolfier fire balloon, made by a man in Maryland and exhibited in a field near Baltimore. The maker promised to go up in it himself, and a great crowd gathered to watch. But when the time came, the balloon lacked enough lifting power to carry him—and that was when a boy in the crowd, young Edward Warren, volunteered to take his place.

Up off the ground he rose, a cable dangling below him to keep the balloon from flying away with him, and the people shouted their hearts out. Edward leaned from the basket and waved his hat proudly. Manned ascensions had come to America!

That was in 1784. Pierre Blanchard, the famous Frenchman, arrived in America less than ten years later and made a great ascent in Philadelphia while President Washington and nearly fifty thousand others watched. He rose a mile in the air, drifted over the Delaware River, and landed at last in New Jersey.

By the 1830's there seemed to be balloonists everywhere, announcing ascensions of their "mighty aerostats" wherever a crowd could be found. One of Charles Durant's ascensions attracted the attention of President Andrew Jackson. Richard Clayton made his great flight of three hundred fifty miles from Cincinnati in 1835, and actually carried mail a few weeks later on a one-hundred-mile flight—the first airmail delivery in the country. C579025 ᴄᴏ. SCHOOLS

There had been accidents, terrible accidents, on both continents. Balloons burst into flames and dissolved in a moment, plunging their passengers down like stones into the earth. Sometimes at ascensions they bumped into nearby buildings and the baskets turned over. Once a runaway balloon took off while its owner was holding onto a rope attached to the netting. He was carried upward, dangling from the rope, until his hands weakened and he plummeted to his death.

But mostly, the balloonists' luck had been good. And the adventuring had gone on—ascensions, fantastic journeys, parachute demonstrations, and showmanship. Always showmanship. In Thaddeus' own home state of New Hampshire, when he was eighteen, a Frenchman named Godard had gone up in a balloon with his wife and a horse. And where was Godard himself? Standing boldly on the horse's back and waving to the crowd! It had been a great sensation.

Thaddeus had met Godard, as well as the great English aeronaut Charles Green, builder of the famous "Nassau Balloon" that carried three men from London to the German Duchy of Nassau in 1836—an astounding trip of five hundred miles in eighteen hours.

It was Green who had first used commercial illuminating gas, known as coal gas, instead of hydrogen for inflating a balloon. It wasn't as light as hydrogen, but it was cheaper and easier to get.

Talking to such men, and to lesser American aeronauts, Thaddeus had realized just how different a successful balloonist had to be from average people.

It wasn't only a question of courage, though the job took plenty of that. Ballooning was a tremendously personal thing, a sort of one-man venture into danger. You checked your own balloon for leaks, you made your own repairs and improvements, you decided when and where it was safe to ascend. And, up in the air, you made the rules as you went along.

You had to have a supreme confidence in yourself, a conviction that you knew what you were doing. You couldn't ask anybody's opinion when the life-or-death decisions were to be made. And besides having confidence in yourself, you had to pass it on to the people who paid to see you ascend or loaned you money for equipment.

It wasn't surprising, then, that many of the balloonists were boastful, jealous men. Each of them thought he was the best. In a way, he *had* to. Each was sure the others were doing things wrong. Each wanted the public to believe he was the greatest.

You didn't have to be something of a show-off to succeed as a balloonist, Thaddeus told Leontine one night, but it helped. It certainly helped.

His little wife smiled at him affectionately.

"Do not worry, Thaddeus," she said, her eyes dancing. "I believe you have the necessary qualities."

For once the noted spellbinder and lecturer was silenced. He looked at her a minute, his jaw sagging. Then they both collapsed into their chairs and laughed until they were weak.

He came into the house roaring, leaping, banging on things.

"Come out, come out!" he shouted. "Come out and meet the newest and greatest aeronaut of them all!"

"Hush, Thaddeus, hush. You'll wake the baby."

"Then I'll wake the baby! At a time like this she should gaze on her father's face. Leontine, I have reached the summit of my ambition. I am owner and captain of a ship of the air!"

It had been a long pull and a hard one. Thaddeus was twenty-six years old now, tall and powerful and utterly confident. In the years since their marriage he had experimented endlessly with pilot balloons, studied everything he could get his hands on, made ascents with every balloonist who came within miles of his lecture circuit. And now the day had come!

"It's a big one, Leontine, really big. And I made an ascension by myself before I bought it. Oh, you should see how it handles."

"But, Thaddeus . . ." Leontine had sobered after her first shout of delight. "Is it a strong one? Is it safe?"

He laughed at her. "No time to begin worrying now, just as my career is launched. Of course it's safe. Well, it is a bit old, perhaps, and some of the seams need attention. But I know exactly what to do to put it in perfect condition. And now listen. I have another surprise for you. Do you know where your husband is going?"

She waited, knowing how he loved his surprises.

"To Canada! The distinguished aeronaut, Professor Thaddeus Lowe, has been engaged to make an ascension at Ottawa!"

"An ascension at Ottawa? But, Thaddeus, you—"

"Ah, you think I am not experienced, perhaps? But you are wrong, madame. Ask the gentlemen who hired me. They will tell you they sought out the most noted balloonist on the continent to help them celebrate the laying of the Atlantic Cable."

He twirled his auburn mustache and stared at her sternly, lips twitching with glee. She tried to frown back at him, but it was too much.

"Oh, Thaddeus, you are impossible. Noted balloonist indeed! At first I thought you were serious."

"Serious, madame? I have never been more serious. The arrangements have been completed. The advance payment from Ottawa helped buy the balloon. I leave next week."

"But your lectures . . ."

"Cancelled, cancelled, cancelled. I am no lecturer. I am commander of a ship of the air!"

So Thaddeus went to Ottawa, where a great celebration was under way. On August 5, 1858, after repeated failure, Cyrus W. Field's dream of laying a telegraph cable across the Atlantic Ocean had become reality. Messages could be flashed like magic from Canada's capital to the palace of Queen Victoria herself. Since everyone was walking on air, what better way to celebrate than by watching a balloonist fly through the air?

He made his first public ascension before crowds of shouting, happy people, and he came back more excited than ever.

"It's only the beginning," he told his wife. "Ah, Leontine, you should have seen me. I was magnificent! The crowds were delighted. I was presented to Cyrus Field himself, and to Samuel Morse, and other great men. And listen—"

"Gently, Thaddeus! Slow down. There is plenty of time."

"But there is not. There are a million things to do. I must arrange more ascensions, get enough money to build a bigger balloon, talk to men with money to invest. Do you know what I am going to do next?"

She threw up her hands. "Heaven only knows. Fly to the moon, perhaps?"

"You are close." For a moment he grew serious. "I will tell you a secret. The signals on the great Atlantic Cable are already growing weak. Something is wrong. I talked with too many scientists to have any doubt. Some of them believe the current is too strong and the wires will burn out."

"And what has that to do with you?"

"Listen. Whatever the reason, the Atlantic Cable is about to become a colossal failure, just as the world has been given a taste of speedy communication. Now they know how valuable it is to find a way to send messages rapidly back and forth across the ocean. It means money to the businessmen, Leontine, great amounts of money. And do you know what they will do when the cable fails?"

"I am almost afraid to ask."

"Then I'll tell you anyway. They will turn to Professor Lowe, the great new aeronaut who will make the dreams of lesser men come true at last. They will be happy to advance money for my project."

Leontine grew pale. "Your project?"

Thaddeus beamed at her. His blue eyes were bright with assurance.

"Yes, my dear. I am going to build the greatest balloon in the history of the world—and fly it across the Atlantic Ocean!"

5

BIGGEST BAG IN THE WORLD

PUFFING slowly through the Maine countryside, the train rounded a curve with a piercing screech of wheels. Thaddeus stirred sleepily and brushed soot from his face.

It was hot in the car, hot and dirty and oppressive, but as he roused himself he felt refreshed and excited. The memories that had been with him when he dozed off came crowding back, and he couldn't help smiling. It was twelve years since he had first seen Portland. Now he was coming back.

In his mind's eye he could see the fifteen-year-old boy he had been, a gangling, foot-weary lad walking resolutely out of the New Hampshire mountains and into a new life. What a headful of dreams he had had, even then!

Well, it had been a long time. The years had been busy ones, and some of the dreams had come true. Not the big one, the flight across the Atlantic. But it was closer. For all his restless urge to get on with it, he had to admit things had gone well.

What if he had known, that day he stumbled wearily into Portland on his way to Boston, that twelve years later he would be returning to stage a mammoth air show as Professor Thaddeus S. C. Lowe, the noted aeronaut?

He could hardly believe it was true. Within a single year, since his first public ascension at Ottawa, he had taken his place as one of the nation's leading aeronauts. Crowds had cheered him in more than thirty ascents. Other balloonists sought him out to discuss the inventions and improvements he was constantly developing for his aircraft. Men came from far and near to buy the balloons he manufactured at his own plant in Hoboken, New Jersey.

The great men whose names he had once held in awe were eager to exchange ideas with him. John Wise himself, whose book on aeronautics Thaddeus had bought when he was eighteen years old, had actually proposed a partnership . . .

Thinking of Wise, he smiled wryly. Perhaps it was just as well nothing had come of that. They would never have got along. Even the letters the older man wrote were irritating. They rambled hopelessly. One moment he would be running on about some great new scheme for making money, and the next he would be lecturing about principles any beginner knew. As if Thaddeus needed to be told the netting was an important part of the balloon rig!

Ever since Thaddeus was a boy, John Wise had been going about the country trying to whip up enthusiasm for his proposed transatlantic flight. Somehow he had never made it, just as he had never been able to persuade the government to use a balloon in the Mexican War. Now he was getting along in years for a balloonist—he was old enough to be Thaddeus' father—and it seemed to gall him to treat younger men as equals.

Thaddeus was ready enough to admit his debt to Wise and the others, but he was fiercely unwilling to be treated as a fool or a beginner by anybody. He had earned his own reputation. For years, before he ever made his first ascent, he had done the homework of his profession. And for all the show-

manship the crowds loved at his shows, he had made it clear
from the first that he was a serious scientist rather than a
mere circus performer.

Other balloonists might be content to do the same things
over and over again, but not Thaddeus. Every show he gave
was to make money for more improvements. On each ascent
he tried new ideas, experimented with new techniques. Aeronautics was a science, not a sideshow. Already he had begun
reporting his meteorological observations to the government
at Washington.

The trouble between him and Wise, he mused, lay in a
clash of personalities. He was ready to honor the older man,
but he wasn't going to knuckle under to him or anybody else.

So now Wise had teamed up with John LaMountain, a man
with plenty of courage but no scientific background, and together they had interested O. A. Gager, the millionaire balloon enthusiast, in their plans. The Trans-Atlantic Balloon
Company had been organized with great publicity, and even
as Thaddeus journeyed toward Portland this hot July day the
balloon *Atlantic* was making a test flight.

That left Thaddeus on his own, but he liked it that way.
When he started on a voyage across the ocean, he wanted
everything done exactly as he himself planned it.

And it wouldn't be long now! Wise might have his balloon
in the air already, but Thaddeus was ready to begin work on
an aerostat that would put the *Atlantic* to shame. Businessmen who wanted profit from airmail flights across the ocean
were giving him handsome backing. After this Fourth of July
show he would settle down to the job of building the *City of
New York*.

But first he would give Portland a day to remember. In the
baggage car, along with the airship in which he would make
his own ascents, were thirty-three small hydrogen balloons,
one for each state in the Union. He would take them up with

him and release them in the upper air currents. What a show they would make!

And while the watching throng roared its approval, he would be considering what he could learn from the speed and distance the little balloons achieved. . . .

A large crowd was waiting at the station at Portland. As the mayor stepped forward to welcome him, the telegraph operator came rushing out of his little office, waving a sheet of paper.

"Professor Lowe! Have you heard the news?"

"What news?"

"About the great flight by John Wise."

Eagerly, Thaddeus read the dispatch. The balloon *Atlantic*, carrying John Wise, John LaMountain and two other men, had just completed a flight of about one thousand miles! It had ascended from St. Louis, Missouri, and landed somewhere in western New York, where the startled inhabitants first thought a piece of the moon had fallen on them.

And, safely on the ground, John Wise had announced triumphantly that the trip proved the *Atlantic* could cross the ocean.

"Well, Professor? What do you think?"

Thaddeus handed the dispatch back to the operator with a flourish.

"Only this, gentlemen. The *Atlantic* will never cross the ocean. That historic event awaits the completion of my own aerostat, the *City of New York*. But another great event must come first."

"And what is that?"

"The Fourth of July show, gentlemen. The greatest aerial demonstration that Portland or any other city on the globe has yet witnessed!"

The reporter from the New York *Daily Times* leaned toward the fire, took a deep breath, and staggered backward with a look of pain on his face.

A fit of coughing overtook him. "And what, Professor," he asked when he was able to talk, "is that villainous-smelling compound? The air reeks of it."

Thaddeus wiped sweat from his forehead with a dirty hand and chuckled.

"It does smell bad, doesn't it? Varnish, sir, varnish to coat my balloon. Don't get too close. That is a very hot fire."

They stood in an open field just across the Hudson River from New York City. It was mid-September of 1859, a little more than two months since the Fourth of July air show at Portland—a show that had been every bit as dramatic as Thaddeus had promised—and work on the great airship *City of New York* was more than half completed. Until now, watchmen had kept the curious away from the Hoboken plant, but Thaddeus had decided the time had come to satisfy the public curiosity.

The young man from the *Times* made a few notes. "Is varnish so important to your plans?"

"As important as my life itself. It is this varnish, made to my own secret formula, that will coat the envelope of my balloon and prevent leakage. But suppose we move into the construction hall. The air there is less . . . ah, villainous."

Together they walked into a building teeming with activity.

In one corner, men worked around a great cane basket twenty feet in circumference. In another stood a giant lifeboat, surrounded by strange-looking equipment. But most of the space in the big hall was taken up by sewing machines—seventeen of them, at each of which a woman worked busily with some of the vast quantities of twilled cloth that seemed to overflow the entire building.

The reporter looked about in awe. "Tremendous, tremendous," he murmured. Then he reached for his pencil again.

"Professor, you must help me put all this in simple terms. Start with John Wise's *Atlantic*. The public knows about it. How does the *City of New York* compare in size?"

Thaddeus' hand went unconsciously to his mustache. He was going to enjoy this.

"Compare, sir? There is no comparison. I am building the biggest aerostat the world has ever seen. The *Atlantic* is sixty feet in diameter, the *City of New York* one hundred and thirty. My gas envelope will hold 725,000 cubic feet of gas. Do you know what that means?"

"Frankly, sir, I have no idea."

"Then I will tell you. It means that, filled with hydrogen, my balloon will be able to lift more than twenty-two tons of weight. Think of it, man!"

While the reporter wrote furiously, Thaddeus poured out a constant stream of facts and figures. Six thousand yards of cloth were being used in the envelope—nearly eleven miles of it. The netting, made from flax expressly for the balloon, was strong enough to support a weight of one hundred sixty tons. The overall height of the airship, from the valve at the top of the envelope to the boat beneath the basket, would be three hundred fifty feet. The . . .

"Professor, please! This is too much for me. These figures are astounding, but help me see the balloon itself as it will appear."

Thaddeus laughed. "I'm sorry. I become easily carried away. Well, sir, picture a big bag covered with netting. Below it, attached to the netting, is a basket. Hanging below the basket is a lifeboat, with a ladder connecting the two. There, without the frills, is the picture."

"And the party itself?"

"We will be in the basket, of course. Plenty of room for all, and sides four feet high with canvas above that. A lime stove, given to me by Mr. O. A. Gager, will keep us warm."

"A stove in a balloon? Isn't that dangerous?"

"Not a lime stove. It furnishes heat without fire. Fire is always dangerous in a balloon, of course, but not as dangerous as you might think. I have lit a candle in a balloon going at the rate of one hundred miles per hour."

"Now, the lifeboat."

"Yes. We will reach the lifeboat by means of a trap door and a rope ladder. It is a Francis boat, thirty feet long, and it will carry one of Captain Ericsson's new caloric engines to control a propeller that we hope will help to regulate our altitude."

"How high do you expect to go?"

"Perhaps three or four miles at the start. But we will not remain that high all the time. I prefer to keep within a distance where I can see folks," Thaddeus laughed. "We will not only see them, we will also drop messages to them. And if by some calamity we are unable to stay aloft—why, there is our lifeboat, ready for use."

"Some calamity like the loss of your hydrogen, perhaps?"

"Actually, we will not be using hydrogen. The problem of getting such a vast quantity makes it out of the question. No, we will use coal gas, bought from the gas company. Not quite as much lifting power, but our margin is more than ample. And the company has assured me it can provide all we need."

"And how many passengers will you carry?"

"That, sir, I am not ready to say. We will announce the names later. But I will tell you that we plan to carry enough provisions for ten persons for six months, in case of a forced landing in some out-of-the-way spot. And a member of the United States Congress may be among us."

The reporter looked at him thoughtfully.

"Professor, in all seriousness, do you expect this desperate project to succeed?"

"Expect!" Thaddeus' blue eyes were burning. "I *know!* Let me tell you I will certainly go on my journey, and just as

certainly I will deliver a copy of your newspaper in London
two days after it is published in New York. Twenty thousand
dollars is tied up in this venture, sir. I can't afford to drown!"

Suddenly all America was talking about Thaddeus and the
City of New York. Newspapers and magazines were full of
news of the venture. The long interview with the *Times* was
reprinted in *Scientific American*. A portrait of Thaddeus,
from a photo by the famed Matthew Brady, appeared on the
front page of *Harper's Weekly*, and a full-page drawing inside
showed the *City of New York* as it would appear in flight.

As for John Wise and the *Atlantic*, they were all but forgotten. Thaddeus had been right—that balloon would never
cross the ocean. John LaMountain had taken it up one day
with a newspaperman, and had been blown three hundred
miles into the wilderness in Canada. Here they had landed,
wrecking the balloon, and wandered about half-starved for
four terrible days before they found their way back to civiliza-
tion. If the ocean was to be crossed in the near future, everyone knew, the job was up to Thaddeus Lowe.

So he worked on while the nation talked—and laughed.
To most of the people it was a great joke, an impossible
dream. They were convulsed with glee at the thought of a
man who actually believed he could fly across the ocean.
Thaddeus was ridiculed in cartoons, poems, and comic magazines. Even the *Scientific American* jeered at him.

"Doesn't all this laughter anger you?" a friend asked him
one day.

He smiled. "Not at all. It serves a very useful purpose—it
directs attention toward what I am doing. Men without
imagination will always laugh at such efforts. But if their
laughter makes others aware of what is happening, then it is
useful."

All through October the work went on. Toward the end

of the month, Thaddeus got a note from a Navy official at the United States Chart Office in New York. The barometers he had requested from the government were ready for the trip.

And so was he. He sat down and wrote a public statement for the newspapers, explaining once more what he had in mind.

"That the airship *City of New York* will accomplish the desired end, I have no reason to doubt," he wrote boldly. Then he answered the jibes of the ignorant by reviewing the history of ballooning in America, and pointed to its great future if men of science and daring were willing to devote themselves to it.

Knowing how jealous other aeronauts were of the attention he was getting, Thaddeus went out of his way to point out their own achievements. He singled out John Wise especially, noting that the older man had discovered the existence of constant west-to-east air currents many years ago.

"Some people may think I am insane, rash, or a seeker after fame," he continued, "but this is not the case. I have for two years coolly considered the subject, and have provided for every contingency. . . ."

Then, his brain racing with still greater dreams for the future, he added a prophecy:

"The time is not far distant when we can travel in the air without the aid of balloons for a buoyant force. I have already devised a plan for an aerial carriage which can be navigated at a high rate of speed as soon as a lifting power can be discovered, the weight of which shall be but one-third of that we now employ. It only requires some shrewd and intelligent inventor to do this, and aerial navigation will become a practical science."

He signed his name with a flourish. Then he gave the order to move the *City of New York* from the construction plant to the Crystal Palace grounds at Forty-Second Street and Sixth Avenue. The time had come.

"On the first day of November," the *Scientific American* reported to the nation, "Mr. Lowe commenced the inflation of his great balloon. . . .

"The gas employed is the same as that which is used for lighting the streets and houses of the city. A ten-inch pipe being laid to one of the mains of the Manhattan Gas Company, the throat of the balloon was tied tightly about its end and the gas began to flow into the biggest bag which the world has ever seen."

Now the nation's excitement grew even higher. Great crowds of New Yorkers paid twenty-five cents each to visit the scene and watch "the great yellow monster," as one reporter called it, begin to take shape.

Letters poured in to Thaddeus from enthusiasts who wanted to make the trip with him. Scientists wrote to ask him to make special observations during his flight. Wise and La-Mountain got their names back in the newspapers by launching attacks against Thaddeus. They called him a humbug, a magician, an unscrupulous adventurer.

One day when he returned home, Leontine showed him a newspaper story mailed to her by a friend. It was from a Southern newspaper. The whole transatlantic enterprise, it said, was part of a secret plot. What Professor Lowe really planned to do was to fly over Charlestown, Virginia, terrorize the people, release the notorious prisoner John Brown, and sail off with him to England.

"It is some kind of a joke, of course," Leontine said, "but I do not understand. Who is John Brown?"

Thaddeus answered absently. "Oh, you remember. That strange old man who raided the government arsenal at Harper's Ferry. An abolitionist. There has been great excitement about him, but it will all blow over."

He had no time to think of John Brown. He had more
urgent problems on his mind, problems he hated to confide
even to his wife. For after all the excitement, after all his
confident boasts, suddenly he could taste defeat—the bitterest
defeat of his life.

And it was all so pointless. To become a laughingstock
before the whole world simply because of a shortage of coal
gas!

In his heart, he had known from the very day the inflation
began that it would not work. The company had promised
faithfully to deliver 500,000 cubic feet of gas in twenty-four
hours. But when the time came, the engineer failed him.

"I must have misunderstood you," he said weakly. "The
largest pipe I have won't deliver much more than 50,000
cubic feet a day."

Thaddeus was thunderstruck. "But that would take weeks!"
he cried. "Do you realize that, however well sealed a balloon
may be, gas escapes constantly from the envelope? While your
pitiful 50,000 feet a day are going into the balloon, so much
will be going out that it may never be sufficiently filled."

The engineer shrugged uncomfortably.

"A mistake . . ." he muttered.

For all his sick conviction of failure, Thaddeus could do
nothing but try. Day after day the slow process of inflation
continued, and day after day the doubts of the public grew.

To make matters worse, the weather turned foul. Winds
whipped the balloon to and fro. Rain made a lake of the
Crystal Palace grounds.

By the latter part of November, Thaddeus had given up
hope. The balloon would never be filled. Then, while he
tried to decide on his next move, the weather decided it for
him. A terrible windstorm came up and buffeted the big
envelope so fiercely that the gas in it had to be discharged to
keep the aerostat from being wrecked.

Now his money as well as his hope was gone. The great

City of New York lay wrinkled and flattened in the muddy water, and Thaddeus did not even have enough money to pay for hauling it away. As the storm continued, ice began to form on the envelope.

Thaddeus made a public admission of failure, blaming the gas company for what had happened. The newspaper reporters, who had learned to trust the tall aeronaut, took him at his word, and the company was roundly denounced. But everywhere Thaddeus could hear the laughter of his critics.

And then, just when everything looked darkest, he was filled with new hope. A committee of scientists from Philadelphia invited him to move his airship to their city.

"But can they provide you with enough gas?" asked one of the reporters when Thaddeus announced the invitation.

Thaddeus was in high glee. "Gentlemen," he said, "the committee is headed by Professor John C. Cresson, who is one of Philadelphia's most distinguished men of science. But do you know what else he is?"

"What?"

"He is president of the board of directors of the Philadelphia Gas Works. And he tells me Philadelphia wants all America to know that, while the city of New York cannot provide me with enough gas, it will be an easy matter for Philadelphia.

"The move will be made, gentlemen. My balloon will cross the ocean. And Philadelphia will get the honor!"

But it was late in the year now, and winter was coming on with a rush. The flight would have to be postponed until spring.

Thaddeus swallowed his disappointment and made his plans. The great airship was carefully stored away for shipment in two freight cars to Philadelphia. He could only hope its days of lying in the water and ice had not weakened the envelope beyond repair. As for himself, he decided, he would go to Charleston, South Carolina, where the weather would be milder, and continue his experimental flights through the winter with smaller balloons.

But why not stop off in Washington on the way and make a few ascensions at the nation's capital? The idea appealed to him. He suggested it in a note to his friend Stephen C. Foster, a Congressman from Maine, whom he had already invited to join in the transatlantic flight.

The Congressman answered promptly. He hoped, he said, that his health would allow him to make the flight to Europe in the spring. But as for ascents in Washington at the present, the weather was much too bad for him to recommend an attempt.

He added a sly joke. "There is, I think, one favorable feature," he wrote. "If you can contrive to draw your balloon over this House of Representatives or the Senate, you can very readily fill it with gas of a kind which God knows the American people will be glad to be rid of—particularly the disunion gas. . . ."

Reading the letter to Leontine, to whom the Congressman had sent personal regards, Thaddeus laughed.

"He's right, of course," he said. "There is more gas in Washington these days than anywhere. All this talk of secession! I hope it will be over by spring, so I can get on with my work in peace."

6

FLIGHT OVER PHILADELPHIA

IT WAS a great balloon, a monster the like of which no man had ever seen before. But would it fly? Was it possible for Thaddeus Lowe, or anybody else for that matter, to get such a thing into the air—and to control it if he did?

All through the winter, America argued.

Self-styled experts rose up on every hand to say the whole thing was impossible. Professor Lowe, they insisted, was a fool or a scoundrel. What had happened in New York proved it. Men like John Wise smiled knowingly when Thaddeus' champions argued he had not had a fair chance. If there had not been a gas shortage, these adversaries answered, there would have been something else. The man was a showoff, a cheap magician trying to defraud the public. The balloon would never get off the ground.

While the arguments raged, Thaddeus himself spent the winter quietly at Charleston, making flight after flight in his smaller balloons. Only in the air could he master the raging impatience within him. To have lost so great an opportunity simply because of a shortage of gas! It was almost more than he could bear.

Sometimes he found himself wondering whether he ever would make the flight he had dreamed about so long. It was a new and disturbing thought. Until now he had never doubted it.

But if matters could go wrong in New York, might they not go wrong in Philadelphia? Would the envelope of the great balloon, already weakened by its long contact with water and ice, retain its strength through the winter? And would the rising sense of unrest throughout America, the smoldering debate over slavery and states' rights, burst into flames that would consume his plans?

No, he told himself. Such a thing could not happen. It was the long delay that made him doubtful. He would put all such thoughts out of his mind and go on with his experimental flights.

By now, control of his craft had become almost automatic. The delicate work of releasing just the right amount of gas through the valve when he wished to go lower, or tossing off ballast in order to rise higher, was second nature to him.

And he was experimenting with other ideas. There was the guide rope, invented by Charles Green—a long rope trailing below the basket to act as a stabilizer. When the balloon was so low that much of the heavy rope dragged on the ground, this made the load lighter and the bag would rise. When it rose so high that the rope was all in the air, the added weight eased the craft lower. A simple device, but it saved both gas and ballast for the aeronaut.

He worked, too, with a device of his own—a long, light cord hanging from the basket and adorned with tiny pennants at regular intervals. By watching which way the little flags blew, he could tell at a glance the direction of the wind at different altitudes.

So the winter passed, and in spring Thaddeus packed up his equipment, gathered his growing family about him, and returned to Philadelphia. As soon as possible, he arranged an interview with the committee that had invited him.

He came home late the night of the interview. Leontine had waited up for him, expecting to learn the date of the proposed flight across the Atlantic, but the look on his face told her it had not been set.

"Did it not go well, Thaddeus?"

He gave her a weak smile.

"Oh, well enough, I suppose." He picked up one of his books from a table. "Science teaches us, ladies and gentlemen," he said, in imitation of his own lecture-hall delivery, "that it is difficult to hasten the movement of large bodies. The gentlemen of Philadelphia are a very large body indeed."

They laughed together at the joke. "The fact is," he went on, "that the committee wants to be sure. It is not as eager to risk its money as I am to risk my life. I have been asked to make demonstrations in smaller balloons, to prove beyond any doubt that there is an easterly air current that can carry me across the Atlantic. As if I hadn't proved it a dozen times in Charleston during the winter!"

But in spite of the fresh delays, he was again full of hope. It was only a matter of time, the time needed to convince the men who would pay the expenses of the trip. The $20,000 collected in New York was gone; now more money was needed for operating costs, for replacement parts, for repairs and workmen's wages and a score of other things. And the men who had the money must be satisfied.

At every opportunity, Thaddeus tried to raise money on his own through balloon exhibitions. In May he put on a memorable show in honor of the first Japanese embassy ever to visit America.

It was only seven years since Commodore Matthew Perry had visited Japan and opened it to outside commerce. Now nearly a hundred Japanese officials were visiting this country to sign a trade treaty and see how the Americans lived. They had never heard of balloons. When they reached Philadelphia, Thaddeus had a show ready to honor them.

His mighty aerostat would not be used, but it was on exhibit for the Japanese to wonder at. While they examined it, John Cresson, president of the Franklin Institute and the man who had invited Thaddeus to Philadelphia, told them through an interpreter how balloons worked.

Then Thaddeus and an assistant, a veteran aeronaut named William Paullin, called the visitors' attention to a small balloon that was being inflated. As they gathered around it, Paullin stepped into the basket, the anchor ropes were cast free, and the balloon shot up so rapidly that the Japanese drew back in amazement.

While they watched it fade to a speck in the sky, Thaddeus himself entered the basket of a large balloon that had been elaborately decorated for the occasion. Suddenly the band nearby struck up the Japanese national anthem, and as the visitors watched in delight, the balloon rose slowly and majestically above them.

The show was such a success that Thaddeus offered to put on an even bigger one in New York City for the Fourth of July.

"I will make an ascension with my new Japanese Balloon," he wrote to the committee planning the celebration, "and in the evening would furnish a large fire balloon to be sent up with fireworks. . . . I would send up in addition during the day, thirty-three pilots representing each state in the Union. Also twelve comic figures representing Whales, Dolphins, Elephants, Serpents, Crocodiles, Porpoises, Flying Dutchmen, Horse Racing—through the air and among the clouds as natural as life. . . . I would furnish another large balloon capable of carrying four to six persons."

But to put on such a mammoth show and still make a

profit for his work, he would need a high fee. He offered to
do it for one thousand dollars.

It was too much money for New York. The committee
turned down his offer. Thaddeus sighed regretfully, thinking
how the crowds would have cheered the wonderful comic balloons, and returned to more serious work.

He awoke the morning of June 28, 1860, with a feeling of
great excitement. Today the big balloon was to make its first
trial ascension!

The committee members were ready at last to put up the
rest of the money he needed. But first, they had said, they
wanted to see the balloon in flight.

Then they would. And, remembering the disappointments
of New York, Thaddeus told himself that today everything
would be different. The weather was perfect, and there
would be plenty of gas. Nothing could go wrong.

Even the name of the balloon was different, and Thaddeus
was glad of it. The old name only reminded him of failure. At
the suggestion of Horace Greeley, the famous editor of the
New York *Tribune,* he had rechristened his aerostat the
Great Western in honor of the entire hemisphere.

This was an especially fitting day for its first flight. On this
same day, the largest seagoing ship ever built, the *Great
Eastern,* was scheduled to arrive in New York Harbor. So it
was up to Thaddeus to make this a day of triumph for the
West.

He dressed quickly and hurried to the Point Breeze gasworks. A tremendous crowd had gathered already. Garrick
Mallery, a tall reporter from the Philadelphia *Inquirer,* hurried forward to greet him.

"I'm ready, Professor. My friends tell me it's suicide."

Thaddeus laughed. "But you still want to go up with me?"

"Oh, yes, I think so. I held a council of war with myself
about it. Now why, I asked myself, should an airship be dan-

gerous simply because it is bigger than any other one in the world's history? Why shouldn't it be safer, for that very reason?"

"My sentiments exactly, Mr. Mallery."

"Besides," the reporter grinned, "I feel it is contrary to nature that my newspaper should not be well *up* in everything."

"Good man!" Thaddeus clapped him on the back and hastened to his work of inspecting, directing, and making everything ready for the ascent of the *Great Western*.

John Cresson himself was directing operations for the inflation. The utility president looked up and smiled broadly.

"Philadelphia will do for you what New York could not, Professor. We'll have all the gas you need inside the envelope in four hours."

"Fine, fine!"

This time, indeed, there was not the slightest hitch. The great balloon needed only 350,000 cubic feet of gas for its brief trial flight without the big lifeboat attached, and the gas poured steadily into the flapping silk. Minute by minute the crowd grew larger—a good-humored crowd, laughing, jesting, a little doubtful but ready to cheer if the balloon did get off the ground.

Now the swollen envelope was tugging at its ropes. Thaddeus dashed about for one final inspection, climbed into the basket, and motioned for an assistant to join him.

"Mr. Mallery, we are ready."

The reporter struck a pose for the benefit of the crowd. "My last dying speech and confession has been made," he joked. "I am ready."

As he climbed aboard there was a flurry of excitement. A workman who was attaching a sandbag to the side of the basket threw down the bag and tried to join the three men in the basket.

"You need ballast," he shouted, "and I can serve as ballast. Let me go with you!"

"Will you agree to be thrown overboard with the other ballast?" Thaddeus roared. The workman paled and drew back.

Suddenly everything was happening at once.

"Hang onto those ropes . . . easy now, let them out a little . . . stand by to cast off . . . what is going on there?"

The basket was already free of the ground, swaying gently to the pull of the bag above it, when two strangers dashed up, shouting wildly, and tumbled headlong into the basket. For all his irritation, Thaddeus couldn't help being amused. Now that the time had finally come, everybody wanted to go up.

"You'll have to get out," he said. Then, seeing the disappointment on their faces, he shrugged. "Never mind. Just keep still and everything will be fine."

He signaled to the ground crew. The last ropes were released.

"Professor," Garrick Mallery said thoughtfully from his position beside Thaddeus, "something seems to be wrong with the ground. It seems to be dropping away from us. I wonder if—*good heavens, we're going up!*"

It was a perfect ascension.

Up through the clear, calm, sunkissed air the *Great Western* rose with majestic speed and grace, the five men in her basket hurrahing and waving flags while the thousands on the ground below went wild with excitement, running here and there in great wavering lines as they tried to follow the course of the balloon.

"And now," said Thaddeus with a calmness he did not entirely feel, "what do you say, sir, to a bird's-eye inspection of Philadelphia?"

The men in the *Great Western* would never forget the hours that followed. Wafted by gentle breezes, the balloon moved through the soft summer air like a great silent ghost,

while all Philadelphia watched. Young Mallery was feverishly writing notes.

"We sail calmly, ravished with ecstasy," he muttered, testing the sound of the words. "Three thousand feet . . . we
look down fondly on Gray's Ferry, Darby and the Park . . .
the city seems to lie asleep, but a vague murmur of life steals
upward toward us—I say, Professor, are we higher now?"

"We are, sir. Do you see that spot down there? The Conti-
nental building."

Garrick Mallery gasped with delight. "And the streets!
They look like a design in geometry!"

Below them, the public squares showed as tiny green
patches in the afternoon light. Spires pointed upward,
touched with sunlight.

"Look, that anthill over there—Girard College!"

"And below you, sir, your own newspaper office. Shall we
give them a salute?" Thaddeus tossed out ballast and the big
balloon shot upward.

"There is an eastward current up here, Mr. Mallery. How
would you like to cross the Delaware at an altitude of a mile?"

The big river lay below them like a ribbon, its bottom
showing clearly through the water. Mallery took the large
spyglass Thaddeus offered him and shouted excitedly that he
could actually see stones in the bottom of the river.

"Why, that is nothing, sir," said one of the two strangers,
who were just beginning to enjoy the trip themselves. "I see
fish moving about in the water."

It was six o'clock when they crossed the river, passed over
Camden, New Jersey, and began to drift eastward toward the
ocean. For an hour or more they watched the panorama below them, calling one another's attention to wheat fields and
cornfields or examining railroad tracks and turnpikes with the
aid of the glass. Once they passed directly through a fleecy
cloud.

"We are higher now, Mr. Mallery. About three miles up, the best my instruments make it. How do you feel?"

The reporter let out a shout of pure joy. "My spirits are almost as high as my body," he cried. "I feel an urge to sing."

He turned abruptly to the rope ladder behind him that led up into the hoop from which the basket was suspended, and climbed it rapidly. Then he began singing, his voice making up in volume what it lacked in quality. The sound echoed from the envelope in such a strange way that his audience in the basket roared with delight.

"I say, there's the moon!" he cried, breaking off his own song. "We are sailing by the light of the moon—and the sun as well!"

It was a novel experience. As the balloon rose and lowered, one sunset followed another.

"How fast are we going, Professor?"

"About sixty miles an hour." Thaddeus looked at his watch and sighed regretfully. "We are near the coast, gentlemen, and it is growing late. I had wished to sail above the ocean itself, but if we do we must set ourselves down in some uninhabited area, and in darkness. Perhaps we should turn back."

He reached for the valve rope and released gas from the top of the balloon. Instantly the big ship dropped toward the ground.

"Almost too fast a descent," Thaddeus murmured. "The air is growing cooler, so the gas has contracted. And look at the dew on the envelope. Its weight helps pull us down."

The big balloon continued to drop. The two strangers were crying out in alarm when Thaddeus, having studied his ship's reaction to his own satisfaction, threw off ballast and brought it up to a safer height.

"And now, at this altitude," he explained, "we find a current that will take us to the northwest. Suppose we begin looking for a suitable landing spot."

They found it soon afterward, in the neighborhood of Medford, New Jersey. Through the gathering darkness they could see hundreds of tiny antlike figures surging toward a spot on the sandflats. As they drew nearer, a buzzing sound grew to a roar, and then individual voices could be heard.

"Listen. They're inviting us to land."

The crowd had assembled as if by magic. Thaddeus let out more gas, the long trailing rope reached ground level, and a dozen men grabbed for it and hung on. At 8:15 P.M., the *Great Western* came to earth.

Garrick Mallery scrambled from the basket first, in a fever to get back to Philadelphia and write his story. In his ears were still ringing the triumphant words Thaddeus had spoken two hours before: "Here at last is the *Great Western* afloat, after all the prophecies against her—and half a million witnesses to the fact!"

The story he was to write would tell the world that the balloon was a tremendous success, that the flight across the Atlantic was assured.

But as the reporter hastened away through the darkness, Thaddeus remained behind examining the fabric of the envelope. In the final moments of their landing, the willing but inexperienced men pulling the rope had grown overenthusiastic. The envelope had come down too rapidly, and had been dragged across the sand and gravel of the flats. And, looking at the great patches of scraped and weakened fabric, Thaddeus felt a sudden wave of cold foreboding sweep over him.

7

THE GREAT RIVER
OF THE SKY

THERE was a screech of wheels as the train worked its way painfully around a sharp curve, and he sat up suddenly, blinking his eyes.

What did the sound bring back?

Now he remembered. Once before he had been awakened in just this fashion by another train going around another curve. The trip to Portland for the Fourth of July show in 1859, that was it.

For a moment he felt weary, remembering how confident he had been then. The flight across the Atlantic had seemed to be within his grasp. Now nearly two years had passed, and the dream was as far away as ever.

Or was it? Surely this time, with the encouragement of one of America's greatest men of science, he was on the right track. But for a man who wanted to fly across the ocean, it was maddening to be on a train bound inland for Cincinnati, Ohio.

He sighed. Two failures in two years . . .

There had been failure in Philadelphia, too, as crushing as

the failure in New York, and despite the success of the *Great Western*'s trial flight.

What a blow it had been! Everything was ready for the journey across the Atlantic. The *Great Western* was loaded, the passengers had said their goodbyes, even the crowd believed this time that the flight would really take place.

And then the wind that had whipped viciously over Philadelphia for two days suddenly increased to a gale . . . the balloon was buffeted beyond its strength . . . and, minutes before takeoff, there was a great tearing sound and the envelope burst.

That was on September 8, 1860. In New York the year before it wouldn't have happened. The silk was new and strong then. But it had been weakened by storms, by ice, by long months of storage, by bruises on the sandflats. Thaddeus' sudden fears that night at the end of the balloon's trial flight had been justified.

What could be done? He had swallowed his disappointment, made such repairs as he could, and tried again on September 29. But it was no use. The old envelope was beyond repair. Somehow he would have to buy new silk, mix more varnish, hire seamstresses, go through the whole lengthy job of making another envelope.

And his friends in Philadelphia had run out of money.

But they hadn't lost faith in him. He took fierce pride in the letter they had sent to Joseph Henry, the famous secretary of the Smithsonian Institution in Washington.

"With reliance upon Mr. Lowe and his plans," they declared, "we cheerfully recommend him to the favorable consideration of the Smithsonian Institution, and trust such aid and advice will be furnished him by that distinguished body as may assist in the success of the attempt, in which we take deep interest."

The most important men in Philadelphia signed the letter, and their words impressed Professor Henry deeply. He read the letter to his Board of Regents, who authorized him to give Thaddeus whatever technical information and advice he could.

So Thaddeus was invited to Washington to meet the great scientist who headed the Smithsonian. And it was Professor Henry himself who suggested the Cincinnati trip.

"It is very difficult to get people to take new devices seriously," he said after Thaddeus had outlined his plans. "Almost every new scientific theory is laughed at."

"I agree, sir."

"And I agree with you that a great eastward air current does exist—but you must prove it to the public. Until you do, they will not support you.

"I suggest this. Go to some inland city and wait until all the conditions appear to be against you. When the lower wind is blowing directly westward, make your ascent. If you can travel east when the lower wind is toward the west, the public will be convinced. Then it will be easy to raise more money for your ocean voyage."

Thaddeus had left Washington full of new hope, and he had wasted no time in carrying out the older man's advice. Now, only a few weeks after the visit, he was on his way to Cincinnati. He would ascend from that city when the winds blew toward the west. Then, when he reached the eastern coast, the world would be convinced!

Stirring restlessly on the train seat, he felt in his pocket for the letter of support Professor Henry had given him. He would want to show it in Cincinnati. It was there, all right, and there was another letter with it. This one he did not intend to show to anyone. He kept it with him for the grim sense of satisfaction it gave him.

To think that old John Wise would have eaten crow!

The very man who had denounced him in all the New York newspapers as a rascal had actually asked Thaddeus to take him along on his flight across the ocean.

He had done it in his own way, of course, a way as arrogant
as ever. "Until within the last twenty-four hours," his letter
had begun, "I never had the slightest belief that you intended
to venture a balloon voyage across the Atlantic. . . ."

Then, after a series of veiled insults, he had got around to
the point of the letter. Since it now appeared that Mr. Lowe
was indeed serious in his plans, of course he would need Mr.
Wise's assistance. Mr. Wise would be willing to serve as scientific director for Mr. Lowe's trip across the ocean.

Looking at the small, cramped handwriting, Thaddeus
could not hold back a smile. In a way he could understand
the crusty old man. Wise, too, wanted to fly to Europe more
than anything else in the world. While he had plans of his
own, Thaddeus was a threat—so he denounced him. But now
that his own plans had failed, he would try to bluff his way
into leadership of Thaddeus' own project.

Well, it wouldn't work. They had gone their separate ways
until now, and they would continue to do so.

He put the letter away, took out some paper, and began
work on a lecture. One of his first jobs in Cincinnati, after
seeing to his balloon *Enterprise,* would be to make a speech
at the Merchant's Exchange. The business leaders of Cincinnati must be persuaded of the importance of his plan. He
would be needing more money soon.

Cincinnati welcomed its famous guest with enthusiasm.
Thaddeus' room at the Burnet House was besieged with reporters from the city's five newspapers, and invitations to
lecture about his balloon poured in. Strangers stopped him
on the street to wish him well. When he spoke before a large
audience at the Exchange on April 2, the *Enquirer* devoted a
full column to his lecture.

It was a welcome change, everybody agreed, from all the
stories about the Southern threat to dissolve the Union. The
new President, Abraham Lincoln, had been in office less than

a month, and an uneasy period of waiting had fallen over the country. What would President Lincoln do about the newly proclaimed Confederate States of America? Would he allow the South to leave the Union? Would he surrender Fort Sumter, as Jefferson Davis had demanded?

Deeply intent on his own plans, Thaddeus had tried to ignore all the talk of conflict. Let the politicians in Washington settle this matter—he had balloons to fly. But it was impossible to ignore the news completely. One night Murat Halstead, the young editor of the Cincinnati *Commercial*, who had become one of his firmest friends, talked with him for hours about it.

"It will all be settled," Thaddeus insisted. "Lincoln is a man who can deal with this crisis. My father is one of his strongest supporters. Only two votes were cast for Lincoln in Randolph, New Hampshire, last November—those of my father and my grandfather."

Halstead smiled. "I agree that he is a good man, but I'm not as sure as you that he can avoid conflict. I tell you, Professor, this crisis is more grave than you are willing to admit. I attended the political conventions last year. I was present at the hanging of John Brown. I can tell you of my own knowledge that violence is afoot, perhaps more violence than any one man can deal with."

Thaddeus refused to be convinced. "War will not come because it must not," he insisted. "Why, sir, it would be a calamity—an unthinkable calamity. We stand on the threshold of great scientific advances. It is not reasonable—"

"Reasonable?" Halstead echoed. "There is no room in this controversy to talk of what is reasonable. Mark my words, Professor. One of these days you will have to open your eyes and admit what is happening."

The hall was a blaze of lights. Murat Halstead had invited many of the most distinguished men of Cincinnati and all

Ohio to his banquet honoring Professor Thaddeus Lowe. The
room was charged with tension and excitement.

Seated on Halstead's right at the table of honor, Thaddeus
plucked absently at a bit of lint on his frock coat and tried to
concentrate on what the gentleman across the table was saying.

"Then you will begin your historic flight tomorrow, sir?"

Thaddeus nodded. "That is my intention, if the winds are
favorable. Everything is in readiness. I have only to call on
the superintendent of the gasworks to begin the inflation."

"But I do not understand, Professor. You wish to fly east,
yet you wait for winds toward the west."

"The surface winds, sir. I propose to demonstrate to America once and for all that in the upper atmosphere there is
always a great eastward-flowing river of air—no matter what
the direction of the currents at the surface."

A hush had fallen around the table. Thaddeus realized he
had raised his voice to lecture-hall volume. A stout man at
the far end gave a short laugh.

"Then the Professor intends to emulate Christopher Co-
lumbus, and to travel west in order to go east. They will welcome you in California, sir, as you fly past."

Thaddeus felt a flush of anger. Deliberately he forced himself to smile and turn away. As the conversation grew general
again, a man entered the room, made his way to Murat Halstead, and whispered excitedly to him. Halstead turned and
grasped Thaddeus by the arm.

"A weather report, Professor," he said in a low voice. "The
wind is blowing fresh and due west. The telegraph reports
the same conditions as far east as Washington. Let us hope
they continue until tomorrow."

Thaddeus thought rapidly. What if the winds changed?
What if more delays arose, delays caused by the snows and
rains that had plagued him ever since his arrival?

Glancing about the table, his eye fell on the stout man

who had spoken so scornfully. An idea came to him. He leaned toward Halstead, smiling excitedly, and began a whispered conversation. As they talked, Halstead too began to smile.

Then the editor of the *Commercial* rose and tapped his knife against his glass for attention.

"Gentlemen, gentlemen! I have important news for you." He paused until the room grew silent.

"Professor Lowe has just been informed that the surface winds are blowing due west, from Washington all the way to Cincinnati. The night is clear. The moon will be rising soon.

"The Professor has made a decision. To allow all of you"— here Halstead's eyes turned directly to the stout man at the end of the table—"to allow all of you to observe for yourselves whether his theories are correct, the Professor has decided to alter his plans.

"He will leave tonight, as soon as preparations can be completed. You are all invited to join us on the lot adjoining the Commercial Hospital, where the balloon will be inflated."

A cheer swept the room. Halstead raised his voice to a shout in order to be heard above it.

". . . may complete your dinners, gentlemen. The Professor promises he will not leave without you. But if you will excuse him, and me, there are things to be done."

As Halstead pushed back his chair Thaddeus rose to his feet, took his high silk hat off a table behind him, and set it at a jaunty angle on his head. Then, arm in arm, editor and aeronaut strode rapidly from the room.

The moon shone down brilliantly on the crowded lot west of the hospital building as Thaddeus, still wearing his high silk hat and frock coat, completed his arrangements. The balloon *Enterprise,* forty-two feet in diameter, was filling rapidly. Banquet guests milled about the busy scene, watching the inflation, shouting good-natured comments to one another, testing and retesting the direction of the warm, damp breeze that blew constantly toward the west.

A shout sounded on the edge of the crowd. Murat Halstead and a companion were advancing, their arms filled with packages.

"We made it, Professor! The *Commercial* has gone to press in time for you to take two hundred copies with you for our friends in the East!"

As the ink-damp newspapers were loaded into the basket, Halstead displayed his other packages.

"You will need provisions. Here is food sent over from the banquet hall, and a jug of hot coffee wrapped in a blanket. The *Commercial*'s most distinguished newsboy must not be allowed to grow hungry while he is delivering his news-papers."

Thaddeus looked at the newspaper and smiled as he read the headline: A NIGHT BALLOON ASCENSION!

"Rest assured I shall deliver your papers, sir," he said. "And now, what time is it?"

"Half past three on the morning of Saturday, April 20, 1861," Halstead answered in a voice grown suddenly grave. "A historic moment, gentlemen."

Thaddeus stepped into the basket of his balloon. "The night is clear," he cried out. "I invite you all to observe the direction of my flight for as long as possible . . . *cast off!*"

With incredible speed, the balloon shot up into the air, hesitated a moment, and began moving rapidly westward. A great cry followed it, in which dismay and encouragement were mingled. Above it all a triumphant voice sounded.

"You see? The balloon goes westward, just as I predicted."

Then suddenly another roar sounded, building rapidly in volume.

"East! East! The Professor is right!"

And high in the air, Thaddeus listened to the shouts and breathed a deep sigh of relief. They had seen, then. Thanks to the moonlight, they had been able to follow his course upward and westward until he struck what he had been waiting for. . . .

The great river of the sky. The great eastward-flowing current he had watched and puzzled over as a boy. The current that would surely take him to the shores of the Atlantic Ocean.

And some day, he felt more positively than ever, across it.

8

FOUR MILES HIGH

NEVER, not even during the *Great Western's* flight over Philadelphia, had he felt such exhilaration. He wanted to shout his triumph into the eerie silence that had fallen over everything when the muffled cries of the crowd below him had faded away. He wanted to dance, to tear up copies of Murat Halstead's newspaper and scatter the pieces over the landscape, to make speeches to the stars and the moon.

Sternly he checked himself. There were observations to be made, notes to be written. Elation must wait.

Altitude? Seven thousand feet.

Temperature? Zero.

Zero? No wonder he was shivering. He drew his frock coat more closely about him, brushed a hand across his forehead, and suddenly gave a great shout of laughter. His hat, his high silk hat, was still on his head. What a pity Leontine could not see him now, speeding through the night clad in a Prince Albert coat and a high hat! She would . . .

Ping-ping . . . ping-ping-ping . . . Wrrrrrr . . .

The sounds came from the envelope above him, a series of sharp pecks followed by ominously drawn-out noises in a lower key. His flesh crawled.

Ping-ping-ping . . .

Anxiously he looked toward the open neck of the balloon, but the moonlight was not strong enough to show him anything. The noises continued. Now a fearful patter sounded on the floor of the basket itself.

Thaddeus groped his way toward it, felt about with his hands, touched something round and cold, and let out his breath in a long sigh of relief.

Ice. Little beads of ice, like hail, were forming inside the envelope, falling onto the silk at the bottom, and rolling down the neck into the basket.

It was easy enough to understand what had happened. On the ground, the gas had absorbed moisture from the damp air. The moisture had been suspended inside the big envelope. When the temperature dropped so rapidly to zero, it had condensed, frozen, and pattered down like a hailstorm.

He remembered a day the previous winter when something like that had happened. Looking up through the open neck of his balloon, he had seen what looked like a miniature snowstorm break out when he had suddenly entered a current of cold air. But it had not been as dramatic as this. He must make a note of it for his report when he landed.

The noises ceased. Groping along the floor of the basket, he tried to estimate the amount of hail that had fallen. A bushel, at least!

And now something else was happening. With the moisture gone, the gas was lighter and the balloon was responding by rising still higher. He felt his way toward the instrument by which he estimated altitude, sighted a star over the top of its mercury column, felt the raised figures on the side, and made his calculation.

Fourteen thousand feet. More than two and a half miles high and still rising.

Far away in the east he saw a streak of light running around the horizon like a stream of melted gold. Sunrise would come early at this altitude. Reaching for one of Murat Halstead's blankets, he wrapped it around himself and settled down to watch.

It was a sunrise he would remember all his life. Never could he forget the exalted feeling, the wonder, the silent grandeur as he looked down on what appeared to be a great hollow bowl and watched it come to light below him. The sun itself filled him with astonishment. It did not dazzle—it glowed, like a giant ball of polished copper. And even as the world grew light beneath him, the sky remained a rich blue velvet in which he could see not only the rising sun but the moon and the stars as well.

At the outer reaches of his vision all around, the horizon appeared perfectly level, like the rim of a colossal bowl. He knew the globe beneath him was convex, but it did no good to tell himself that fact. It still seemed to drop down from the horizon everywhere.

Well, not everywhere. As the light grew he could see something far off in the distance that looked like a big hill rising above the line of the horizon. He looked at it, puzzled, until finally he worked it out. That single stabbing peak was not a hill, not one mountain, but an entire range of the Appalachian Mountains.

Again he checked his instruments. Altitude, 18,000 feet. More than three and a quarter miles high!

Only one thing disturbed him. He had intended to go almost due east, but the winds were carrying him southeast. As the mountains drew nearer, this tendency seemed to increase. The currents around and between the great ranges—the Cumberland, the Allegheny, the Blue Ridge—were altered by the mountains themselves, it appeared.

The mountains had another effect on the balloon. Approaching a towering rise, Thaddeus suddenly felt himself shooting breathlessly up, up, up, almost too rapidly for him to keep his breath. The action, he realized, was like that of swiftly flowing water when it strikes a large boulder in a stream—a tremendous splash upward.

This time, he felt, he was higher than he had ever been in his life, and when he took a reading he was awestruck. Twenty-two thousand feet. Now he was *more than four miles above the earth.*

Like a great bird the balloon swooped upward over the mountain, and then plummeted downward with incredible speed. Within a single minute he had lost a complete mile of altitude and was gasping weakly from the reaction.

The craft steadied itself and soared on, and again Thaddeus was struck by a sense of unreality about it all. Here in an open basket, plunging along at a speed he hesitated even to guess, everything was utterly still. No breeze tugged at his face or blew the papers he scattered carelessly about while he wrote. For he was not traveling *through* the air, but *in* it, like a fish floating down a stream.

He decided to estimate his speed with the aid of an instrument for measuring latitude and longitude. The result brought a look of unbelief to his face. Again he made his calculations. He shook his head, unable to accept the results. Then he looked downward along the rope that hung a hundred feet below the car and watched it sweep like a whispering shadow over farms, fields and woods. Never, he knew, had he traveled so fast. He looked a third time at his figures, then spoke aloud in a voice filled with wonder.

"A *hundred* miles an *hour* . . ."

An urge to speak to someone overcame him. He was not sure where he was, he told himself. Perhaps he could find out. But there was another and stronger reason. This swelling sense of exultation was too much to endure alone. Through the night he had experienced such wonders that he must make some kind of contact with man again to regain his sense of reality.

He took up his glass and studied the ground before him. Far ahead on the slope of a mountain he saw some men plowing in a field.

Carefully he opened the valve and let the balloon descend toward them. As he went downward, he entered an area of still air and drifted more and more slowly until he stood almost stationary above them.

"Hello!"

The men started with surprise. He saw them look all about, in every direction except upward. Then, shaking their heads in puzzlement, they returned to their work.

Holding in his laughter, he shouted again.

"Hallooooo! What state is this?"

One of the men stepped back from his plow, faced a nearby patch of woods, and put his hands to his mouth.

"Virginia!"

Thaddeus reached for a ballast bag. "Thank you," he cried, and poured a large amount of sand down toward them. As the balloon shot upward he burst into laughter. The men on the ground suddenly looked up, shouted in alarm, and began running toward the woods as if their lives depended on it. Not until years later would Thaddeus learn of the rumor that swept the whole area like wildfire that day—a tale of a great hog's bladder in the sky, passing overhead with the speed of light, a sure sign that the end of the world was coming.

On and on swept the balloon, clearly deflected now in a southeasterly direction by the mountain currents. Thaddeus found himself doubling up and laughing like a small boy at the memory of the panic he had left behind. He knew it had been a childish stunt to play, but the long hours of loneliness had cried out for relief. "Hallooooo!" he shouted again and again, beating his silk hat weakly against the basket in delight.

At last he gasped wearily, realizing he had come close to hysteria, and peered again through his glass. In the distance stretched a great body of water. He rubbed his eyes, looked again, and put the glass down with shaking hands.

The Atlantic Ocean! The sun was not yet directly overhead, and already he had reached the ocean.

For a moment he wrestled with a wild urge to continue, to make this voyage the one that would electrify the world, to sail on, on until he had reached Europe or Africa. But he knew he must not. He was not prepared for the journey; the balloon was not big enough; he had already let out too much gas.

Reluctantly he released gas, descended, and found a current that would take him back inland. Below lay acres of rice fields, too wet for a satisfactory landing. He drifted along for some minutes before he saw an area he liked better, a high field in which a number of men were working. As he drew nearer, he was surprised to notice that many of them carried muskets.

He came down fast, and his arrival touched off a great cry of alarm, followed by a general rush in his direction.

"Gentlemen, I salute you. May I ask where I am?"

They drew nearer warily, their eyes startled and suspicious.

"South Carolina. Where are you from?"

"I come from Cincinnati, Ohio."

The largest of the men pointed his gun directly at Thaddeus.

"Stranger," he said in a voice high with tension, "you may be telling the truth, and then again you may not. Even if you are, we don't want you around here. From Ohio, eh? Well, get out of here quick or I won't be responsible for what happens."

Thaddeus stared at him open-mouthed.

"But all I want, sir, is to find a railroad on which to load my balloon and—"

The weapon flickered ominously. "There's no railroad near here. Get that thing back up in the air quick and go tell Abe Lincoln he'll have to do better than that."

"Abe *Lincoln?*"

"Git!"

Maybe it was a dream caused by the high altitude. Surely this wasn't the world as he knew it. But whether it was dream or reality, Thaddeus decided abruptly, the time had come to move on. Half a dozen other guns were pointed toward him now. He snatched up a big bag of ballast and tipped it over the edge of the car.

"Hey, mister!" a voice shouted as he shot upward. "You've dropped your baggage!"

It was the final touch of absurdity. Thaddeus roared with laughter as the balloon moved upward. Then he grew sober. Lincoln? Of course, of course! If he was in South Carolina, he was in secessionist country. But was the situation so bad that men actually went armed into the fields?

Ruefully he confessed to himself that he had not followed the news as closely as he should have during the past week or so. What was it Murat Halstead had been telling him before the banquet last night? Fort Sumter had been fired on by Confederate troops . . . had been evacuated . . . and the event had led Lincoln to issue a call for troops to be used against the seceding states.

And there was something else. He remembered it now. "This very day," Halstead had told him, "the President declared a blockade of Confederate ports. Professor, we stand at the brink of calamity."

But he had not listened, had not asked himself how his own future might be affected by that of his country. Like so many others, he had gone blindly on, planning his own plans, trusting to others to bring the nation back to sanity—actually impatient, not at the terrible threat to peace, but at the distracting influence it had on his own plans!

Well, now he would learn for himself where Thaddeus S. C. Lowe, aeronaut, fitted into the events of the day. If Murat Halstead was right, he was flying over enemy territory, and about to land in it.

A low ridge rose out of the flatland below him, and he maneuvered the *Enterprise* toward it. So much gas was gone from the balloon now that it was urgently necessary to land soon. This appeared to be as good a place as any, here in a field whose edges were dotted with rude cabins and whose workmen, as far as he could tell, did not carry guns.

Cautiously this time, and with no thought of playing pranks on the people below, he drifted downward, dangling his anchor rope over the side of the car. Scores of birds, alarmed by his approach, took wing with harsh screeches. Negroes and white men in the field heard the noise, looked up, and ran for cover toward the cabins. The balloon moved slowly across the field, only a few feet above the ground, until the anchor took firm hold in a rail fence. Envelope and basket came to a sudden shuddering halt.

"Hello!"

Here and there he caught a flash of cautious movement in or near the cabins. He waited patiently for the sensation caused by his arrival to die down.

"Help! I need help! Will someone come and steady my car for a landing?"

The silence lengthened out until Thaddeus felt his flesh crawling. Then a door creaked on its hinges, and he turned in time to see a tall young white woman emerge and walk toward him. She came on resolutely until she stood directly beneath the balloon.

"What can I do?"

"Thank you. I want someone to hold my car steady while I let more gas out of the balloon."

"All right." She turned toward one of the cabins. "Come on out and give me a hand!"

As if her example had shamed them to action, men began appearing from all sides and walking toward the balloon. Thaddeus saw or three of them put shotguns down beside the fence before they joined in steadying the car. At least he was not in danger as immediate as he had been on his last stop.

"Well, here goes." He opened the valve wide, and the remaining gas came out in a rush. For a moment confusion threatened; the gas had a foul smell, and some of the men seized their noses and cried out in suspicion and alarm. Thaddeus motioned for them to move out of the path of the drifting gas.

An elderly Negro broke into a sobbing wail.

"Sperrits! Sperrits!"

Others took up the chant, and Thaddeus realized his first job would be to convince the simple people around him that he was only a man. Hastily he reached into the basket of food Halstead had given him and took out cakes, crackers, and slices of cold meat, passing them around to those nearest to him.

"This is a balloon," he said, speaking slowly and distinctly. "I have been riding through the air in it since before daybreak this morning. I am very tired, and I have been cold. It is freezing cold up in the air. Look." He reached for an india-rubber water bottle, cut it open, and displayed the ice inside, frozen in the shape of the bottle.

Almost at once he realized it was a mistake.

"He's a devil!" someone cried. "How else could that big block of ice get through the neck of the bottle?"

"No, no." Hurriedly he unrolled the blankets around the coffee jug and poured some of the hot coffee onto the ground, letting everyone see the steam rising from it. Then he reached for a copy of the *Commercial*.

"I tell you I'm an ordinary man like any of you," he cried. "I flew here from Cincinnati. Look, here is a newspaper from there. Look at the date on it."

A man moved reluctantly forward and examined the paper.

"He's right."

Thaddeus sighed in relief.

"And what I say is, if this Yankee can do what he claims, then he's too dangerous to run around loose. I say we shoot him."

There was a general movement toward the guns along the fence. The young woman who had first approached the balloon pushed her way to Thaddeus' side.

"You needn't worry," she said in a scornful voice loud enough for all to hear. "They won't do anything to you. Most of them are cowards. All the brave men around here have gone off to war."

War!

"Then you will help me?"

"We'll help you." She turned to the others. "Nobody harms this man," she said. "Come on, now, let's do what needs to be done so we can take him to the county seat."

She turned back to Thaddeus.

"You understand, of course," she said quietly, "that you are now a prisoner of the Confederate States of America."

9

PRISONER
IN THE CONFEDERACY

THE tall young woman may well have saved his life. Under the contempt in her voice the men had fallen back, undecided. Before they recovered, Thaddeus reached into the basket of the *Enterprise* and pulled out a large Colt revolver.

"The lady is quite right," he said. "I am no enemy, but under the circumstances I am ready to consider myself a prisoner until the authorities have questioned me. What is the name of your county seat?"

"Unionville, South Carolina."

"Unionville." Thaddeus smiled at the irony. "Then take me and my balloon there. I will go quietly. But let me warn you that if any man makes a hostile move toward me or my equipment, I will shoot."

He turned to the young woman.

"Madam, I am at your service."

"Very well." She looked about the clearing. "Some of you men get a wagon and load his equipment while we feed him."

Thaddeus was taken to a one-room cabin nearby. Inside, he sat at a rough table on a three-legged stool while the ashes in a big open fireplace were pushed aside. An iron oven was brought out, and when it was opened Thaddeus smelled the delicious aroma of cornpones.

"Eat hearty, stranger," somebody said. "These corn dodgers are better with butter, but that's all gone to the army. We have a little molasses, though. You can't beat dodgers and molasses."

A small boy watching him grinned bashfully. "You ought to be here in the summertime, Mister, when we have blackberries. These dodgers sure taste good then!"

Thaddeus was touched by their hospitality. Excusing himself, he went out to the wagon and brought back all the food remaining in the basket of the *Enterprise*.

"You have shared with me. Let me share with you."

Delicacies of North and South were eaten and praised by all. Then they went outdoors where the wagon awaited, a team of six mules hitched to it, and the entire party set out in a holiday mood on the ten-mile journey to Unionville.

The tall young woman told him goodbye outside the cabin.

"These men will take good care of you," she said, looking at them with warning in her eyes. "If they don't, they'll answer to me when they get back."

All in all, they were a strange sight. Still wearing his silk hat and Prince Albert coat, Thaddeus sat in the wagon, while men clad in bluejeans and mounted on scrawny horses or mules rode on each side. Nodding drowsily, Thaddeus had to keep reminding himself it was not some ridiculous dream. These men and their mounts might be too old or weak to join the army, but they were in dead earnest about delivering him a prisoner to the county seat. And when he arrived, what then?

The jolting, dusty ride seemed endless. Time after time he fell into an uneasy half doze from which he was awakened in the gathering dusk by the clanking of harness chains, the occasional shouts of his captors, or a bone-shaking bump as the wagon dropped into a deep rut.

Was this the way his dream of flying across the Atlantic would end—with conviction as a spy, solitary confinement in some Southern prison cell, or even worse? He shook his head impatiently. Even now he could not believe the land was really at war. Surely it would all be settled in a few days. Sanity would prevail. But in the meantime . . .

"Whoaaa, there!"

The wagon stopped abruptly and he fought his way back to wakefulness. It was dark now. They were in a small village. The entire company had halted before a rickety building with a sign, barely visible in the light of a lantern, proclaiming it the county jail.

"Get the jailer!"

Two men jumped down from their horses and pounded on the door. A man came out, blinking sleepily, and a low murmur of voices drifted back to the wagon. Straining his ears, Thaddeus could hear only an occasional snatch of the conversation.

". . . right down out of the sky . . ."

". . . so I said he's a Yankee sure, sent down here by old Lincoln to make trouble . . ."

". . . keep him in there till we can get him properly tried and shot . . ."

Then the voice of the jailer, still sleepy but emphatic, rose above the rest.

". . . tell you I just can't do it. If he's what you say he is, there's no use in putting him here anyhow. He'd just break out. This old jail wouldn't hold anything. Besides, it's full of abolitionists already. No place for him."

"But what are we gonna do with him?"

"Take him to the hotel and leave a guard with him. That ought to keep him out of trouble. Then we can figure out something in the morning."

The suggestion seemed to please his captors. Thaddeus suspected they had been a little reluctant to lose the limelight by turning him over to the jailer. This way they could be important for a while longer. Shouting importantly, they ordered the wagon and escort to drive on.

The hotel was a long two-story affair with a porch running its entire length. Thaddeus studied it while the same two men who had spoken to the jailer dismounted and went in to consult the landlord. He was about to doze off again when they returned.

"Bring him in."

Rough hands reached for him, and in a sudden burst of sleepy anger he shook them off. Setting his hat firmly on his head, he stepped down, buttoned his frock coat, and strode toward the hotel with all the dignity he could muster. Candles and lamps blazed in the main reception room. As he hesitated, almost blinded, a well-dressed man stepped forward.

"Now, then. This is my hotel and I want to see the man you say—why, Professor Lowe! It is you, I believe?"

Thaddeus looked at him in amazement. He could not remember ever having seen this man.

"Yes. I am Professor Lowe." He tried to keep the weariness out of his voice.

"You will not remember me, Professor, but I could never forget you. I made an ascent in your balloon at Charleston last year. One of hundreds, of course—and I will never forget the thrill it gave me. Professor, let me shake your hand."

Thaddeus felt a hand clasp his own warmly. "A spy indeed!" The man's voice had grown sharp. "Do you men realize you have been mistreating one of the world's foremost aeronauts?"

The sudden about-face in the situation had left Thaddeus' captors as stunned as he was. They looked at one another blankly, shuffling their feet. Through his weariness, Thaddeus felt a surge of wry amusement.

The shuffling continued. The men were clearly embarrassed. One of them coughed, reddened, and began a speech of apology. Instantly Thaddeus' own attitude changed. After all, these were simple men who had been doing what they thought was their duty—basking, no doubt, in a feeling of importance they seldom enjoyed, but doing their duty all the same. And certainly they had not harmed him in any way. Considering the circumstances, he was more indebted to them than he had realized.

"There is no occasion to apologize," he said warmly. "Gentlemen, you have really done me a service in bringing me and my equipment here, a service I would have been glad to pay for. Now, let us forget all this unpleasantness. You must be hungry after our long ride. Allow me to be your host. Sir, could a dinner be served to the entire company at this late hour?"

The landlord smiled. "It can, Professor, and it will."

It was a gay dinner. Guests from the hotel, roused by the excitement, dressed hastily and came down to see what was going on. The party grew. Thaddeus found himself a hero, telling everyone present about his journey. Maps were brought out and consulted, times were checked, and abruptly a breathless hush fell over the entire gathering.

Even Thaddeus felt a chill of fresh excitement as he looked up from the maps to make his announcement.

"I left Cincinnati at half past three in the morning," he reported. "These gentlemen who brought me here will testify that I landed near Unionville at one in the afternoon of the same day. That is nine and a half hours. And our best estimate of the distance traveled is—*one thousand two hundred miles.*"

"Good heavens!" one of the guests breathed. "More than a hundred miles an hour! Is it possible?"

Thaddeus smiled at him sleepily. Suddenly he felt over-
come by exhaustion. It seemed months since he had left
Cincinnati, months in which he had had neither rest nor
sleep. His eyelids drooped and he found himself unable to
focus clearly on those about him.

"Gentlemen, I must rest. But first let me repay the escort
that brought me to this place."

There were protests, but he insisted. Then he followed the
landlord wearily upstairs to a room, removed his outer
clothes, and fell across the bed.

A pounding on the door roused him. Stiff and aching, he
stumbled to the door.

"You must get up at once, Professor." The landlord looked
gravely worried.

Thaddeus yawned. "What time is it?"

"Seven o'clock."

"Seven o'clock! But I do not care to rise before noon. I
am very tired, sir. Now, if you will excuse—"

The landlord put a hand on his arm.

"Professor, you must wake up at once. Remember where
you are. Last night I was able to assure those present that you
were not a spy, but matters have changed this morning.
Rumors have gone through the town. Feeling is high. A
crowd has gathered about the hotel, and its leaders refuse to
go away. Because they have not seen you for themselves, they
think something suspicious is afoot."

Rubbing his eyes, Thaddeus went to the window and
looked out. It was true, all right. A milling crowd stood outdoors, clustered around the long porch and looking angrily
upward, searching the windows of the hotel for a sight of him.

"I am considered a man of some importance in this town,
Professor. If you will come out and show yourself with me, I
believe we can quiet them."

Thaddeus nodded thoughtfully. "Give me just a minute."

He dressed hurriedly, noting with surprise when he looked into the mirror that his face was terribly sunburned from his balloon ride. Then he hastened downstairs with the landlord. In the parlor he met a group of Unionville's most prominent citizens—the newspaper editor, the sheriff, a member of the legislature.

"Our plan, Professor," the sheriff told him after they had all talked for a while, "is to take you for a ride through the town. There are about three thousand people in Unionville today on account of you. Some have come from sixty, eighty, or even a hundred miles away. They saw your balloon or heard news of it. They are curious, mostly, and I believe the sight of you in our company will satisfy them that you are not an enemy. But I want us to move promptly before the situation gets out of hand."

"Surely not before breakfast?"

The sheriff smiled grimly. "Better to delay your breakfast, sir, than never to eat it at all. Shall we go?"

Thaddeus and the sheriff rode on the front seat of the carriage, with the editor and the landlord in the rear. As they made their way slowly through the crowds, all four of them bowed to right and left as if they were receiving an ovation.

The plan worked. Seeing the stranger calm and confident in the company of the town's leaders, the onlookers changed their attitude from hostility to interest. Back and forth along the town's streets the carriage went until at last the crowds grew satisfied and began drifting away.

The sheriff insisted that the ride continue until fully two-thirds of the bystanders had disappeared. Then they returned to the hotel for breakfast and another round of questions far more searching than those that had been asked the night before.

It was Mr. Thomson, the member of the state legislature, who finally put into words the doubts that Thaddeus had seen on more than one face while he was describing his journey.

"Surely you will forgive me, Professor, if I ask whether you have any tangible evidence that you left Cincinnati the morning of the same day you landed in South Carolina?"

"Of course, sir. Let me see. I will gladly pay the cost of a telegram to Cincinnati asking for confirmation. Or perhaps you would be satisfied with one of the copies of the Cincinnati *Commercial*, dated April 20, which I brought with me?"

"A copy of the *Commercial!*" cried the editor. "That will be proof enough for any of us."

After Thaddeus had produced a newspaper, the last traces of doubt left the faces of his new acquaintances and they settled down to giving him a full day of hearty hospitality.

Mr. Thomson, whose son had left a few days before at the head of a regiment bound for Virginia, invited him to dinner. A certificate of the hour and place of his landing was drawn up and signed by witnesses. The newspaper editor invited him to visit his offices. Noting signs on every side that Unionville was deeply committed to war, Thaddeus was impressed by the kindness its citizens displayed to the Northerner who had appeared so dramatically among them.

The next day, Monday, a train bound for Columbia came through Unionville. Half the town was at the station to see him get aboard with his balloon and instruments.

He expected to change trains at Columbia for Washington. As they pulled into the station he noticed a great crowd had assembled—no doubt to cheer the large number of soldiers on the train, he supposed. But when he slung one of his instruments over his shoulder, dismounted, and began walking toward the baggage car to see to the transfer of his balloon, he discovered his error.

"There he goes!" It was a fierce, excited shout.

"Look at him! Got a gun on his back!"

He was the one the crowd had been waiting to see. Thaddeus felt his flesh crawl.

He was at a loss. He had only minutes to change trains, but if he ran or seemed to hurry in any way it would only make the temper of the crowd worse. Well, he would have to take his chances.

He set out at a brisk pace toward the baggage car.

Steps sounded behind him and a hand fell heavily on his shoulder. Turning, he saw a tall, bearded man with a pistol.

"Halt. You are my prisoner."

"Your prisoner? And where do you wish to take me?"

"To jail, of course."

Thaddeus looked about him. The crowd had surrounded him by now, and there was no doubt its temper was bad. Even jail would be better than the hands of a mob.

"Very well."

The big man hustled him safely through the jeering throng and into a carriage, and in a few minutes he was being locked in a jail cell. He was brought out again a quarter-hour later and taken to a large room for interrogation by Columbia's mayor and councilmen.

In all honesty, Thaddeus had to admit to himself that he was receiving remarkably fair treatment from people who were sending their young men off to war. The officials of Columbia regarded him kindly.

"We must be sure who you are, sir," the mayor explained. "In such times as these it is our clear duty to take no chances, but we have no wish to do you harm. Is there anyone you know in Columbia who can identify you? Perhaps you know some of the professors at our college?"

Thaddeus shook his head ruefully. "I am afraid not. But would it help if they questioned me about my work?"

The mayor agreed to the plan. Several faculty members from the college were brought to the jail, and in the scientific discussion that followed, Thaddeus convinced them beyond doubt that he was indeed who he said he was.

Smiling, the mayor rapped for order.

"I am happy, sir, that we have been able to establish your identity and reputation. You represent people with whom we are at war, but I trust we have not lost our sense of generosity. You are here by accident and we will do our best to help you return to your own people. Wait a moment."

He reached for a pen and wrote busily. Then he handed Thaddeus a slip of paper.

"Let us hope that this will serve as your passport through the Confederate States."

Thaddeus read the words on the paper:

This is to certify that Prof. T. S. C. Lowe, now accidentally in our midst, is a gentleman of integrity and high scientific attainments, and I bespeak for him the courtesies of all with whom he may come in contact, and trust that this letter, to which I have affixed the seal of the City of Columbia, S. C., will answer as a passport for him through the Confederate States of North America.

W. H. Boatright, Mayor.

Thaddeus felt a lump rise in his throat.

"Believe me, sir, I appreciate this more than—"

"It is my privilege. But now we must see what else we can do for you, Professor. Your troubles are not yet over. There will be no more trains to Washington until this war is ended."

10

DREAMS DIE HARD

"I REPEAT, sir, this rebellion is no concern of mine, and it must not stand in my way. My entire career has been directed toward one great achievement, the crossing of the Atlantic Ocean by air. Do you think I will let a miserable political disturbance interrupt my work?"

As he talked, Thaddeus restlessly paced the floor of his room in Cincinnati's Burnet House. The trip back from the Confederacy had been a wearing one. With train service to Washington cut off, he had been forced to return by slow stages through Tennessee and Kentucky, in crowded trains that stopped constantly along the way to pick up uniformed men and wildly excited civilians. He was incredibly tired. Deep lines of fatigue etched his face, but his blue eyes burned hotly with determination. Murat Halstead looked at him with concern.

"You are worn out, Professor, and little wonder. You have been through a great deal in the past six days—your historic flight, your arrest, your narrow escapes, your long journey back through Rebel country. When you have had a little rest—"

"Rest! There is no time for rest. I have work to do."

The young editor eyed him curiously. "You still refuse to understand the gravity of the situation. And yet you saw for yourself. You traveled through a great portion of the Confederacy. You tell me that even in Nashville and Louisville the talk of secession was strong. Can you honestly believe this is no more than a—what did you call it?—a miserable political disturbance?"

"You do not understand. I must—"

"You must face the truth, Professor. Of course it is hard for you. It is hard for all of us. Men all over the country must put aside their plans and dreams. The nation is in danger and you can serve it in a special way. As I told you, I have important friends in Washington. You must let me arrange for you to meet them. Think what balloons can do to shorten this war!"

Thaddeus threw himself onto his bed. "You talk of war, but there is no war. No shots have been fired except at Sumter. I doubt if there ever will be any real fighting."

"Shots were fired in the Baltimore riot. Men were killed. What do you call that?"

"Rioting. Not war."

"You saw the Southern troops going to Virginia."

"A gesture, sir, only a gesture. And even if there is fighting, it will be short. You know yourself it will all be over within ninety days."

"I know some men are predicting that." Halstead's face was grim. "I also know in my heart that they are terribly mistaken. This is not merely an insurrection, Professor. It goes far deeper. I expect a long war, a bloody war."

"All the more reason, then, for me to stay out of it. Surely you realize the importance of what I am doing."

With an impatient gesture, Murat Halstead rose from his chair. "Very well. But think about what I have said. And when you are ready—"

As he left the room, Thaddeus rose wearily to his feet and resumed his pacing.

While the nation prepared for war in the days that followed, Thaddeus went stubbornly ahead with his work, the dream of the Atlantic flight still bright in his mind. He must make more flights, raise more money, convince investors that nothing would halt him from a fresh effort.

On May 8, twelve days after his return from the Confederacy, a large crowd gathered in the vacant lot beside the hospital. Cincinnati's newspapers had spread the word: before his flight across the ocean, Professor Lowe would make another ascension in the *Enterprise*. He would carry three passengers for a short distance, put them down, and then continue his journey alone. Perhaps, if conditions were right, he would go all the way to Washington, D.C.

Inflation of the balloon proceeded without a hitch. Junius Browne, a reporter for the Cincinnati *Press,* was first into the basket. He was followed by W. W. Wirt, a businessman who had caught the ballooning fever, and J. C. Freno, a visiting Philadelphian who hoped to become an aeronaut himself.

"All set?" Thaddeus turned for a last wave to the crowd, and climbed into the basket himself.

"Cast off!"

The balloon rose steadily with its heavy load, and the four men in the basket waved their hats until the crowd was out of sight. The flight had begun.

From the beginning, it was somehow different from all the others Thaddeus had made—a quiet, peaceful interlude that made any thought of war for the lovely land below seem like a terrible dream. Slowly they drifted eastward, the setting sun at their backs. While Browne and Wirt drank in the sights of the countryside, Thaddeus chatted idly with Freno about mutual friends in Philadelphia.

The sun was setting when they sighted a large farm, descended, made the cable fast to a big apple tree, and looked about them.

They were in Clermont County, Ohio. From the nearby farmhouse a man hastened, smiling broadly.

"Come in, strangers! You're just in time for dinner."

It was a delicious farm meal, and during the quiet night that followed, Thaddeus slept better than he had in weeks. In the morning, after breakfast, he and his fellow travelers strolled contentedly back to the big apple tree where the balloon waited.

Thaddeus had planned the overnight stop for two reasons: to give his passengers a pleasant ride, and to see how well the *Enterprise* would keep its buoyancy overnight. When they examined it he was delighted. Even with a heavy coat of dew on the envelope, the balloon was straining at its anchor. He turned to the others.

"Well, gentlemen, I must be on my way. Wish me luck."

Wirt put a hand on his arm.

"Let me go on with you."

Thaddeus looked at him in surprise. "Yesterday's voyage was not enough?"

"No. Let me keep you company."

"Then climb aboard, sir. Climb aboard."

With the help of the two men on the ground, the *Enterprise* took off once more, riding low into the sun. As the dew on the envelope evaporated, the travelers rose higher and higher until, at an altitude of two miles, Thaddeus found the eastward current he was seeking.

"Now I must check our course carefully, Mr. Wirt. I do not wish to land among the secessionists again."

For a long time he studied his instruments and maps. Then he shook his head regretfully.

"Luck is not with us. If we stay in a current fast enough to take us to the coast by nightfall, we shall be obliged to land in Virginia. But if we find a more northerly course, we will go too slowly."

"Then what do you propose to do?"

Suddenly Thaddeus grinned like a schoolboy. "What do you say we simply enjoy ourselves today? We'll find a likely town and see if we can stir up a little excitement."

It was still early morning when they drifted to earth near Higginsport, Ohio. They had been seen before they landed. A shouting party of gentlemen hurried out to meet them, bargained eagerly with Thaddeus, and then towed the balloon triumphantly into the town square by its anchor rope.

Everyone in the little town turned out for a celebration. Guns were fired in salute. A musical group known as the Hiawatha Brass Band assembled hastily and began playing military airs.

"Who wants a ride?"

"Come on, let's have some fun!"

The men went up first, three and four at a time. Then a lady in the crowd said boldly that she would like a ride if the Professor would promise to keep the balloon safely anchored to the earth.

All through the morning the rides went on. More rope was brought to stretch the anchor cable to seven hundred feet. Picnic lunches were spread, and the fun continued into the afternoon. Once the members of the little band swarmed over the basket and ropes and ascended a short distance, playing "Yankee Doodle" as the *Enterprise* staggered aloft.

Now a group of citizens arrived on the scene from just across the Ohio River in Kentucky. Would Thaddeus allow them to move his balloon to their town, Augusta, and give the citizens there a thrill? They had taken up a purse already. They could offer him two hundred dollars.

"Good enough. Let's go!"

Six strong Kentuckians towed the balloon to the ferry landing, Thaddeus riding in the basket high above them. The balloon was anchored firmly to the ferry and the shouting party climbed aboard the little boat.

And then, halfway across the river, trouble came. A strong breeze sprang up and the *Enterprise* suddenly surged back toward the Ohio shore, dragging the ferry and its terrified operator with it.

The flatboat hit the river bank with such force that half its length ran up onto the land, and Thaddeus could hear the wails of the ferryman rising through the roar of the wind.

No one was hurt, but the expedition was clearly at an end. Thaddeus let the gas out of the balloon and, with Wirt's help, began packing for the return to Cincinnati. All the way home they chuckled over the day's adventures.

It was May 10 when they got back to Cincinnati, and when Murat Halstead visited Thaddeus at the Burnet House that night the look on the editor's face made him forget the fun at Higginsport.

"There is fighting in St. Louis right now," Halstead told him. "Union forces are engaged with Missouri militia. Rioting has broken out in the city. Professor, how long can you ignore a war?"

For a while longer he tried. He announced a series of short ascensions to raise money, and began dickering with the Canadian city of Hamilton, Ontario, which was planning a great celebration of Queen Victoria's birthday. Perhaps they would be willing to pay him a handsome fee for an ascension.

But even as he planned, he was losing enthusiasm for the idea. A sick feeling grew in him that he would not cross the Atlantic this year or any other year. And with it grew a deep dissatisfaction with himself.

Halstead was right. How long could he go on closing his eyes to the events around him, trying to live a life apart from the crisis that was enveloping everyone else? Did he even have the right to insist that his nation did not need him?

At last he sent the editor a message, begging him to come
to the Burnet House.

"You are right," he admitted abruptly when Halstead
walked into his room. "I suppose I have known it all along,
but it was hard to face." He smiled miserably. "The dreams
of a lifetime die hard, my friend. But I thank you for helping
me bury them."

Halstead gripped his hand tightly. "I knew it was only a
matter of time. Listen. Salmon Chase, the Secretary of the
Treasury, is a good friend of mine. I shall write to him at
once."

Now that he had made the decision to give up private ballooning, Thaddeus felt better. He was packing to leave Cincinnati when the letter from Canada reached him.

It was ironic. At first the committee at Hamilton had re-
sisted his offer. But now, when he had all but forgotten it
and turned to other plans, the members had decided to accept. All arrangements had been made for his appearance for
the celebration. The money would be waiting.

Ruefully he gave the news to Halstead.

"I will go, of course," he said. "They expect me. But when
it is over I will return to Philadelphia and do nothing until
I hear from you. If they want me in Washington, I will be
ready."

The Queen's birthday was on Friday, May 22. Thaddeus
arrived in Hamilton on Wednesday, eager to get the job
done, and fell to work at once preparing for the ascent.

From the beginning he was dogged by trouble. By Friday a
high wind was raging. All through the morning Thaddeus
postponed the hour of the ascension and consulted restlessly
with the celebration committee.

By noon the delays had upset the entire day's program.
Shouts that the balloonist was a fraud began to be heard in the
crowd. Thaddeus lost his temper, was soothed by a member
of the committee, and finally agreed to make a short talk to

the people. Weather conditions made the ascent impossible, he announced. The balloon would go up the following Wednesday afternoon instead. They could take his word for it.

That night the telegraph wires brought word that troops from Washington had occupied Alexandria, Virginia, and that a Federal officer, Colonel Elmer Ellsworth, had been shot and killed while he was hauling down a Confederate flag in the city. Thaddeus ground his teeth helplessly. He should be in Washington!

The days dragged endlessly. His nerves grew raw as he thought that a letter from Halstead might already be awaiting him at Philadelphia. But he had promised an ascension at Hamilton, and he would see the job through if it took all spring.

Wednesday came, and with it more troubles. The winds were still high. There were fresh delays. Again the cry of "Fraud!" was raised in the crowd. Ordinarily, Thaddeus would not have paid any attention, but now he stormed furiously to the chairman of the celebration committee.

"Are you going to keep order here, or not? I do not like to be insulted."

"We are doing our best, Professor. Believe me, most of your audience has complete faith in you."

Thaddeus sighed wearily. "I am sorry. There is too much on my mind these days. My country is in great trouble."

At last, two hours after the scheduled time, the wind eased and the *Enterprise* was ready. Suddenly a man thrust his way through the crowd.

"Take me! I want to go with you!"

It was always happening at ascensions. Thaddeus was too tired to argue. "All right. Get in."

The man crawled over the side of the basket and sat down in the bottom. Thaddeus stood on the opposite side, directing the release of ropes, and waved his hat at the crowd as the balloon rose. The fickle crowd cheered noisily, and the stran-

ger in the basket rose to an uneasy crouch, looked out, and
waved weakly.

The *Enterprise* soared away in the direction of Niagara
Falls, and Thaddeus gave a great sigh of relief. The job was
done!

Two hours later he landed at the little Canadian village of
St. Anne's, told his passenger goodbye, and began packing
away his balloon. As he worked, his spirits began to rise.

Murat Halstead's letter was waiting for him when he
reached Philadelphia, and there was also a brief note from
Professor Joseph Henry of the Smithsonian. After a joyous
reunion with Leontine and the children, Thaddeus turned
eagerly to the mail.

"Listen to this, my dear. Professor Henry writes that the
Enterprise is needed in Washington. Confederate troops are
near the capital, and from the balloon I could report their
size and location."

Already he was tearing open the other letter.

"And what does your champion from Cincinnati report?"

Thaddeus' eyes raced over the words.

"He has recommended me strongly to Secretary Chase, and
Chase has talked to the Secretary of War and other high officials about my work. Listen to what Halstead writes: 'I am
fully convinced that you are the man, and that you could at
once render your country and your science a very essential
service.' "

Leontine pursed her lips thoughtfully. "What does he
mean when he says you are the man? Are there other balloonists there?"

"Yes, and some of them have strong friends in Washington,
too. Secretary Chase said there is little doubt that an aeronaut
will be used, but there is a difference of opinion as to which
one will be chosen."

"And what will you do now?"

Thaddeus gave her a quick hug. "I am forever saying good-bye. Come and help me pack. Halstead says I should go to Washington at once."

11

YOUNG AERONAUT
IN WASHINGTON

DUST rose in clouds from the cobblestones of Pennsylvania Avenue as a company of uniformed horsemen rode past the corner of Sixth Street. As the clatter of hoofs grew fainter, a tall, ramrod-straight figure in frock coat and high silk hat emerged from the National Hotel, hesitated, and moved southward across the street toward Constitution Avenue and the Mall. Twenty-eight-year-old Thaddeus Lowe had returned to Washington with a new dream.

Midway across Pennsylvania Avenue he paused to watch the passing of a noisy squad of soldiers clad in gaudy red and blue Zouave uniforms, their blouses glittering with gold lace.

"Come on, boys, we're heading for Richmond!"

"Wait till I get my hands on Jeff Davis!"

Thaddeus stared after them thoughtfully as they made their way toward the Capitol, whose great unfinished dome rose in the distance. Then he shook his head and walked on.

In the few months since his last visit, Washington had changed unbelievably. Soldiers in many kinds of uniforms thronged the streets. Bands marched. Trash littered the alleys. Wagonloads of supplies clattered over the cobbles. Everywhere the preparations for war could be seen—and everywhere, Thaddeus observed, was disorder and confusion.

How could President Lincoln and his generals turn these thousands of untrained, boisterous soldiers into an army? The Confederates were already massing only a few miles across the Potomac in Virginia. Could order be brought out of this chaos in time to save the Union?

The question gave him a fresh sense of urgency, and unconsciously he increased his stride. He was almost running when he reached the Mall and crossed the flowered grounds of the Smithsonian Institution. Not pausing to admire its high red towers, he hurried inside.

Joseph Henry, secretary of the Smithsonian and the nation's most honored scientist since Benjamin Franklin, greeted him warmly.

"My dear Thaddeus, you have no idea how happy I am to see you. You got my letter? I have talked to your friend Halstead. We both feel you can do your country a great service in these terrible times."

"I hope I can, sir. That is why I am here. What do you suggest?"

Instead of answering, Professor Henry sighed heavily.

"Turmoil! Turmoil is everywhere, Thaddeus. I have never seen such disorder and uncertainty. The President is under a tremendous burden. For a while we thought Washington would be captured by the Confederates before any of our soldiers arrived. Well, the soldiers are here now, but I am not at all sure we are safe. . . ."

He seemed to have forgotten Thaddeus for the moment. He walked to the window of his office and looked out. Then, with another sigh, he turned.

"But that does not answer your question. What do I suggest? I suggest that we sit down and talk for a while about

how balloons may best be used in this conflict. Halstead tells
me you are sure you can use the telegraph for messages between the air and the ground. I want to hear your plans. Then
I will go personally to Mr. Cameron, the Secretary of War,
to see what can be done."

"Thank you, sir. Halstead has advised me to see Mr. Chase
as well."

"It can do no harm. The Secretary of the Treasury has little
to do with the armies, of course, but he is a powerful politi-
cian. You may know he hopes to be nominated for the Pres-
idency in 1864." Professor Henry threw up his hands in
exasperation. "Even at a time like this, my dear Thaddeus,
one must remember politics."

For an hour or more they talked. From time to time the
older man nodded vigorously as Thaddeus outlined the plans
and ideas that had filled his brain since he had turned his
thoughts to war.

"Planning, my boy—that is what this country needs now.
And you have planned well. We must have demonstrations,
here on the Mall where all Washington can see them. We
must find the right men to help put your plans into effect.
Balloons can be of great value to us, or they can be of little
more use than toys. You know that you are not the only aeronaut on the scene?"

"Halstead suggested there are others."

"There are. James LaMountain is trying to get attention
at the War Department. A brave man, no doubt, but this calls
for more than bravery. And there is James Allen of Rhode
Island. I hear he is already in Washington with a balloon."

"And John Wise?"

Professor Henry shook his head. "I have heard nothing
from Mr. Wise. Perhaps it is just as well. He is no longer
young, Thaddeus. We need young men with strength and
imagination."

He rose from his desk and offered his hand. "There are many things to be done. We must get busy."

The next day Thaddeus called on Salmon P. Chase in the vast Treasury Department building near the White House. Minutes after the interview, he was dashing into the Smithsonian.

"Great news, Professor Henry! Mr. Chase says he will arrange a personal meeting for me with President Lincoln himself!"

Joseph Henry smiled. "Excellent. And I have news myself. The Secretary of War is most interested in your plan to send telegraph messages by balloons. As you know, the War Department has just been connected by telegraph with the Navy Yard and our outlying encampments. Wires are even being carried across the Potomac into Virginia."

"Then I could—"

"Exactly. If you ascended at Arlington, you could report your observations by telegraph directly to Secretary Cameron's office. It would be something utterly new in warfare."

At the eagerness on Thaddeus' face, Professor Henry smiled. "And now for my biggest news. The Secretary wants a demonstration. You may spend $250 to prove you can send telegrams from your balloon. And I am directed to observe your work closely and make a full report to the War Department."

During the days that followed, Thaddeus was busier than he had ever been in his life. The *Enterprise* arrived from Philadelphia and was taken to the Mall and unpacked. Arrangements were made to inflate it from a gas main on the Armory grounds. Working feverishly, Thaddeus gathered a handful of assistants and began preparing his equipment.

Late on the afternoon of Tuesday, June 11, he returned to his room at the National Hotel to find a note awaiting him. Wearily he opened it. A moment later he was scrambling frantically through his bag for a fresh shirt, the words of the message echoing loudly through his mind:

"Secretary Chase wishes you to go up to the President's House this evening as early as you can after getting this note."

He would never remember just what words were spoken in that first meeting with Abraham Lincoln. A combination of excitement, weariness and something close to awe made it all like the dimly recalled fragments of a dream.

He could remember the big upright desk in the President's office, and the long oak table where the Cabinet met, and the armchair between the windows where Abraham Lincoln sat listening and occasionally asking a question. But later, whenever he tried to tell Leontine the details, he could only shake his head in defeat.

Professor Henry had gone with him. Thaddeus had raced down the streets of Washington, coattails flying out behind him, to find his friend and adviser. Together they had gone through the big gateway in the iron fence, past the statue of Thomas Jefferson, and into the White House itself. They had been escorted by Mr. Chase past dozens of politicians, inventors, and political hangers-on into the President's office. And, after the introductions, Joseph Henry had spoken highly of Thaddeus' accomplishments.

Then it was up to Thaddeus—to answer the President's penetrating questions about the military use of balloons by the French more than sixty years before, and to explain his own plans for taking a telegraph wire up into the air with him for the first time in history.

Suddenly it was all over and they were leaving the White House. Still feeling the firm pressure of Abraham Lincoln's hand on his own as they parted, Thaddeus turned to Professor Henry.

"What do you think, sir?"

Joseph Henry laughed. "I think you won him over, young man. I think he will be watching from the White House windows when you make your ascent."

The President watching! Thaddeus vowed to himself that nothing would keep the experiment from being a perfect success. He had worked hard before; now he redoubled his efforts, checking and rechecking everything, inspecting the *Enterprise*'s envelope, examining cables, consulting with telegraph experts on the size of wire to be used. Day after day he pushed himself almost beyond endurance.

The newspapers were full of stories about the coming experiment. Most of them were enthusiastic. A new day was dawning for the Union, they predicted, a day in which observers high in the air would see and report every move of enemy troops. Surprise attacks would be a thing of the past. Commanding officers would know what was going on everywhere on the field of battle.

But one report disturbed Thaddeus deeply. General Winfield Scott, general in chief of the Union armies, was said to have no interest in balloons at all. A reporter quoted the old man as saying they would not amount to much.

It was a bad sign. How could balloons be made a great new weapon if the nation's highest military officer was ready to dismiss them so casually?

But on June 18, a week after his visit with the President, he was too busy to think of General Scott. The time had arrived. The grounds of the Columbian Armory swarmed with army observers, newspaper reporters, officials of the telegraph company and the gasworks, and curious citizens.

The center of interest was the *Enterprise,* now almost fully inflated. Two large American flags had been painted on its envelope, and the car below it was filled with equipment— telescopes, signal flags, wires, ropes. A giant reel nearby held a roll of fine wire covered with green silk insulation. One end of the wire, with a small instrument for sending and receiving messages, would go up with the balloon, unwinding off the reel as the *Enterprise* rose. The other end was connected

with a telegraph line that ran between the War Department
and army headquarters at Alexandria, Virginia.

Through the crowd came Herbert Robinson, a skilled
telegraph operator, and George Burns, superintendent of the
telegraph company .

"We are ready, Professor. The wires are working perfectly."

"Excellent. The inflation has just been completed. Shall we
enter the car?"

A moment more and they were off.

The day was ideal. As the balloon rose slowly in the air,
Thaddeus knew in his heart that everything else would be
ideal, too. Nothing could mar this event.

Slowly the men below let out the mooring ropes. And as
they did, Thaddeus could see the telegraph reel unwinding
slowly and smoothly, paying out the precious wire.

An uneasy thought struck him. "You are sure, Mr. Burns,
that we will have sufficient current?"

"I see no reason why we should not, Professor. There is a
strong battery at the War Department end of the wire."

The top of the White House was clearly visible now. Thaddeus watched it for a while without moving. Then, as the
balloon rose still higher, he placed a telescope to his eye.

"Gentlemen," he said quietly, "this is a momentous occasion. We are about to begin an aerial reconnaissance on
behalf of the United States of America, and to report our
findings in the first telegraph message ever sent from a balloon."

Herbert Robinson stirred behind him. "Shall I send a trial
message to the War Department?"

Thaddeus nodded. Then he thrust out a hand to halt the
operator. "No. Wait, Mr. Robinson. The first message should
go to the President."

He swept the horizon with his glasses and paused a moment
in thought.

"Here is the message. Head it 'Balloon *Enterprise*,' and

address it to the President of the United States. Tell me when you are ready for me to go on."

The chattering of the telegraph key was loud in the air.

"Ready."

Slowly, Thaddeus dictated the message:

"Sir: This point of observation commands an area nearly fifty miles in diameter. The city, with its girdle of encampments, presents a superb scene. I have pleasure in sending you this first dispatch ever telegraphed from an aerial station, and in acknowledging indebtedness for your encouragement for the opportunity of demonstrating the availability of the science of aeronautics in the military service of the country."

"And how shall I sign it, Professor?"

"T. S. C. Lowe."

The key fell silent. The three men in the balloon suddenly found themselves looking at one another as tension grew unbearably.

The silence continued.

But there *must* be an answer! Without it, for all they knew, the experiment had failed. Had something gone wrong after all? Had the thin wire broken on the reel, or the battery failed? Was all the work in vain?

Thaddeus took out a handkerchief and wiped his face.

"Gentlemen—"

A sudden brisk noise interrupted him. For a moment no one moved. Then the three men in the balloon gave a great shout of triumph.

The telegraph was chattering briskly, confirming receipt of the message at the War Department.

Joseph Henry's voice reached Thaddeus above the shouts of all the others as the *Enterprise* rode slowly down toward the ground. The elderly secretary of the Smithsonian was capering on the Mall like a boy of twelve.

"You did it, Thaddeus! I knew you would! Come on down here where I can shake your hand!"

As the basket touched ground, the two men flung their arms about one another in triumph. For a while, as Burns and Robinson left the balloon, the cheers were so great Henry could not make himself heard. Then, as Thaddeus prepared to step out of the car, Henry raised his voice.

"Wait! Are you in the mood to go up again?"

The crowd heard the question, and listened eagerly for Thaddeus' reply.

"A dozen times if necessary, sir. But why?"

"I have just received a message from the President. He would be happy for you to have the *Enterprise* towed to the White House."

The cheers swelled up again as Thaddeus bowed, handed the telegraph key to Mr. Burns, and signaled his ground crew to let out the mooring ropes.

And while Washington watched in amazement, the *Enterprise* was towed grandly to Pennsylvania Avenue and along that wide thoroughfare to the grounds of the White House.

From the basket Thaddeus studied its windows curiously. In one of them stood a tall figure, watching intently.

The President of the United States!

When the bag was brought down and the ropes were made fast, Thaddeus stepped out and was greeted by a member of the White House staff.

"Allow me to congratulate you, Professor. We all saw your ascension. A wonderful demonstration, sir, wonderful."

"Thank you."

"And now, sir, will you come along with me? I am directed by President Lincoln to invite you to spend the night at the White House."

12

THE ROAD TO MANASSAS

ACROSS the Potomac from Washington, the Virginia countryside slept fitfully in the darkness. Sleepy Union sentries patrolled the raw, newly dug entrenchments of Fort Runyon, guarding the approaches to the Long Bridge which led into the heart of the capital. North of them on the heights overlooking the river, lights shone down the hillside from a magnificent white-columned mansion.

It was four o'clock on Sunday morning, June 23, 1861.

A few weeks before, this had been peaceful land. Now, from the Chain Bridge north of Washington to Alexandria on the south, it swarmed with soldiers. The white-columned mansion, lately the home of Robert E. Lee, was the headquarters of Brigadier General Irvin McDowell, commanding officer of the Union army.

Thirty miles away, Confederate troops were massing around Manassas Junction. The waiting was almost over. Soon now the war would become real.

A low rumble of sound alerted a sentry who guarded an intersection on the Columbia Turnpike. Peering through the false dawn, he made out a strange sight. A great shape, bouncing gently up and down, was approaching him. It looked as big as the Capitol dome itself.

"Halt! Who goes there?"

The weird form jolted to a halt, and from the confusion of figures below it a tall mustached man stepped forward.

"Thaddeus Lowe, aeronaut, with the balloon *Enterprise* and a detail from the Eighth New York Infantry."

The sentry sighed in relief.

"Oh, it's you, sir. I saw you up in the air yesterday. You gave me a start." He chuckled. "Advance, balloon, and be recognized. Where are you going this fine day, sir?"

"We are ordered to Falls Church for reconnaissance."

"Falls Church? That's closer to Manassas than I'd like to get right now. Well, just head out the turnpike and turn right at Bailey's Cross Roads. Mind you don't get yourself shot."

The men holding the mooring ropes moved forward, stumbling as a gust of wind shook the balloon.

It would be a slow march to Falls Church, Thaddeus told himself, and if the wind grew worse there would be trouble aplenty. But never mind that. He was in action at last.

Thinking back over the events of the past few days, he grinned wearily. Action? He had had plenty of it, beginning in the White House itself!

Abraham Lincoln had talked to him for hours that night after the *Enterprise* made its telegraph flight. The President wanted his ideas about organizing a balloon corps, about directing artillery fire from the air, about designing a portable apparatus to inflate balloons in the field. And the next day there had been ascensions from the White House lawn, with President Lincoln and his cabinet members watching.

It was after one of these ascents that Thaddeus, red-eyed with fatigue, had been approached by a young officer wearing the insignia of the Topographical Engineers.

"Professor Lowe? I'm Captain Whipple, attached to General McDowell's headquarters in Virginia. The general is very interested in you and your balloon."

"I am glad to hear it. Perhaps he can influence General Scott's thinking."

"Oh? You have seen the general in chief?"

"Only briefly. The President sent me to his office this morning, but he had no interest in balloons. So I came back here to continue my demonstrations."

Whipple smiled ruefully. "The Topographical Engineers have known General Scott's feelings about balloons for some time. But we are the ones who must make field maps, and our attitude is different. We have been asking questions about you and the Rhode Island balloonist, James Allen. You may know he made a brief ascent last week."

Thaddeus nodded. He had heard of Allen's work.

"And the chief of our bureau, Major Bache, has been in contact with another aeronaut. John Wise. You know him, Professor?"

"I know him."

Noting Thaddeus' wry expression, the captain laughed. "Well, never mind that. Let's get down to business. General McDowell wonders if you could haul your balloon over the river into Virginia and make some ascensions. What do you think?"

"Captain, that is just what I have been working for. But you understand, of course, that the *Enterprise* was not made for military use. A stronger balloon is needed for work at the front. If the government will only authorize it, I can build one in a few days."

"I understand. But first we want to see what you can do in the field. Could you use the *Enterprise* temporarily?"

"Of course. When you are ready, give me time to have it reinflated, and a detail of men to tow it, and I will be at your service."

"Thank you. You will be hearing from me."

That had been last Wednesday, and since then events had moved rapidly. On Friday, Professor Henry filed his War Department report, praising Thaddeus' work and urging a trial in the field. That same evening the order came to report to McDowell's headquarters. On Saturday the *Enterprise* was towed across the Long Bridge and Thaddeus made an ascension at Arlington Heights in the presence of General McDowell and his staff.

And now, with scarcely time to think about his success, he was advancing toward the Union outposts in the interior of Virginia, to prove himself in the field.

Well, he would show them. He would . . .

"Halt! Who goes there?"

They were approaching a railroad crossing guarded by a small detail of Union soldiers. Thaddeus halted his party and identified himself.

"You're going to Falls Church, sir? But how will you get there?"

"Why, along the turnpike to Bailey's Cross Roads, and then right to the church."

The sentries looked at one another.

"Professor," said the noncommissioned officer in charge, "I have bad news for you. We're the last pickets on the pike. If you follow it any farther, you might run into Rebel patrols. You'll have to cut through the woods."

"But I can't do that. We couldn't get the balloon through safely."

The corporal shrugged. "Then what will you do?"

"Watch and see."

Briskly, Thaddeus returned to his waiting detail. For a moment he and the men from the Eighth New York talked in low tones. The infantrymen seemed puzzled at first, but as

Thaddeus continued to explain his plan they broke into broad smiles.

"Sure thing, Professor! Just tell us if we do anything wrong."

While the corporal and his men at the railroad crossing watched in slowly dawning understanding, the *Enterprise,* with Thaddeus now riding in the basket, began rising higher and higher above the turnpike. Twenty feet . . . thirty . . . forty . . .

"Hold! I have a clear view of our front and flanks. If I see any sign of the enemy as we advance, I will let you know. Forward, gentlemen!"

The men holding the ropes resumed their march. One of them broke into a song and the others took it up. Over the tracks and along the turnpike into the unknown territory ahead moved the *Enterprise.*

As it disappeared in the distance, the corporal at the railroad crossing scratched his head in wonder.

Nothing could go wrong for him on that expedition, it seemed to Thaddeus.

The *Enterprise* lurched triumphantly onward, its very appearance in the air so majestic and awesome that a Confederate patrol at Bailey's Cross Roads took to its heels in dismay before he had time to call a halt. On the party marched to Falls Church, where Captain Whipple was waiting, and for the rest of the day and all day Monday the *Enterprise* made one ascent after another.

At first the weather was too bad for successful observations, but the telegraph wire was tried and worked with great success. And when the skies cleared on Monday, Thaddeus took up Major Leyard Colburn, a skilled mapmaker, who charted every road, stream and house in the surrounding country from his lofty vantage point.

General Daniel Tyler, commanding the brigade at Falls

Church, looked at the map and beamed with satisfaction. Promptly he sent off an enthusiastic telegram to General Mc-Dowell, reporting that Thaddeus' flights had convinced him of the value of balloons in the field.

Captain Whipple himself was delighted. "Your job is done here," he told Thaddeus on Tuesday. "You have proved your point beyond question. Now, if you will take the *Enterprise* back to Washington, I will get busy. I will meet you there tomorrow at the Bureau of Topographical Engineers, and by then I should be ready to discuss permanent arrangements with you."

Thaddeus returned to the capital to find the newspapers full of his exploits. Some of the stories were wildly inaccurate. One in particular said he and General Winfield Scott had gone up together and flown over Manassas Junction, where they espied Jefferson Davis, Robert E. Lee, and General Beauregard sitting down to breakfast. The thought of the seventy-five-year-old general in chief flying with him over enemy lines left Thaddeus convulsed with laughter.

But then, when the future looked so bright, the blow fell. Captain Whipple summoned him to a conference, and the moment Thaddeus walked into the engineer's office he knew something was wrong.

"Professor, I have been going over your estimates with my chief, Major Bache," Whipple began, toying uneasily with a pencil on his desk.

"Yes, sir?"

"Ah . . . I believe I told you he has been in contact with John Wise also?"

Thaddeus' eyes grew suddenly alert. He nodded.

"Mr. Wise has given us estimates too. He believes he can build a satisfactory balloon at a cost that is two hundred dollars less than your own figure."

"And?"

"Of course we must choose the lower offer." Whipple

cleared his throat. "However, Professor, keep in touch with us. We may wish to use you to operate Mr. Wise's balloon after it is made."

Thaddeus felt anger sweep over him like a fever. For a moment he was silent, thinking of his weeks of work at the capital. Then he rose.

"Very well, sir." His voice was so cold that Whipple reddened. "Save your two hundred dollars. A balloon is a delicate machine that must be built with the utmost care. Of course you can get a cheaper one than I offered. But don't ask me to operate it. Do you think I would risk my life and reputation in a cheap contraption made by a man in whom I have no confidence?"

He could hear Whipple stammering protests behind him as he stormed down the corridor and out of the building.

His first thought was to give it all up, to wash his hands of Washington and return to his family and his work at Philadelphia.

He had not wanted to get involved in this war in the first place. Very well, then. Now that he had used up so much time and money in a vain attempt to be of service, he could leave with a clear conscience. Perhaps, even yet, he could renew his dream of flying across the Atlantic. Perhaps . . .

But in his heart he knew he would stay. Deep below the anger was a conviction he could not shake off: that a man cannot evade his own duty by blaming others. No, he would have to try harder than this before he could leave with a clear conscience—if, indeed, he ever could.

Grimly he returned to his work. He gave the *Enterprise* a new coat of varnish and began a new series of demonstrations at his own expense on the Smithsonian grounds.

The days passed and became weeks. Congress assembled in special session on July 4, and the Mall was full of senators and congressmen admiring the big balloon. Occasionally Captain Whipple and his chief, Major Bache, appeared in the crowds, watching the work with deep interest.

But still no word came for Thaddeus from the Topographical Engineers, from the War Department, or from anyone else in authority. Only Professor Joseph Henry remained to cheer him up. Time after time in those trying days the secretary of the Smithsonian revived his flagging spirits.

"Be patient, Thaddeus. They cannot long ignore you."

"I wonder, Professor. Wise is scheduled to arrive here soon with his new balloon. John LaMountain has been ordered to Fortress Monroe. I hear that James Allen will take two balloons to Alexandria to serve under McDowell."

"True. But—"

"And here I remain," Thaddeus burst out, "only a few miles from our forces in the field, ready and waiting! I could be making daily observations in Virginia. I could be building a new balloon, or proving that my design for a portable gas generator will work. But no, I sit here giving demonstrations to the curious!"

"Your time will come, Thaddeus. Mark my words."

And then, just when even Professor Henry had begun to grow doubtful, an urgent message arrived on July 17 from Captain Whipple. The Union forces were on the move toward Manassas Junction. John Wise and his long-awaited balloon had not arrived. James Allen's balloons had burst, both of them, before he had been able to make one successful reconnaissance.

Thaddeus, the message said, was directed to inflate his balloon at once and proceed with it to the interior of Virginia.

For a moment, after the first thrill of triumph, Thaddeus was furious.

"Look!" he stormed, thrusting the dispatch into Professor Henry's hands. "Not a word of apology, not a by-your-leave. I am *ordered* to Virginia with a balloon which I told Whipple a month ago is unsuited for long service in the field. He expects me to wait around hopefully, and then come running the first time he crooks his finger at me. And he offers not so much as a detail of men for the work!"

"I know, Thaddeus. But isn't it what you have been waiting for, all the same?"

Thaddeus opened his mouth to protest. Then he paused, and broke into a rueful laugh.

"You are right, sir. As always. I will hire a detail at my own expense."

The preparations took hours. Once he had decided to swallow his anger, he threw himself into the job and worked with a sense of desperate urgency. The Union army was advancing. The great battle everyone expected could not be far off. What were his personal feelings compared with the service he could give his country?

By the time he had rounded up a detail, examined the envelope of the *Enterprise,* checked all his equipment, and planned his route of march, he had forgotten his resentments entirely. As the neck of the balloon was connected to the gas main for the inflation, he found himself hot with excitement. This time he would not be going out to make a mere demonstration. This time . . .

"Wait, wait! Turn off that gas main!"

The director of the gas company was pressing through the little knot of men working over the *Enterprise.* Thaddeus turned toward him with a sick sensation in the pit of his stomach.

"What is wrong?"

"Nothing is wrong, Professor Lowe. But I am directed to tell you that your services will not be needed, and the gas must not be wasted. John Wise has arrived in Washington with his new balloon. Your orders have been cancelled."

Never, Thaddeus told himself that night, not even when

the envelope of the *Great Western* burst in Philadelphia, had
he suffered such a crushing blow. The anger, the shame that
he had fought against during the long weeks of waiting, rose
up now in a great wave that could not be subdued. He slept
restlessly, and rose the next day determined to put Washington behind him for good.

This time even Joseph Henry did not urge him to try
again.

Bitterly, as the weekend approached, Thaddeus went about
his preparations to leave. There was a limit, he told himself,
to what any man could be expected to endure.

Friday passed, and Saturday. His arrangements were almost
completed now. He took no interest in anything about him,
even the reports that John Wise was running into delay after
delay with his new balloon, that he still had not even managed to get out of Washington with it.

He was sleeping late on Sunday when a tremendous pounding at his hotel door awakened him. A man who had assisted
him at his ascensions on the Mall burst excitedly into the
room.

"Professor, have you heard?"

"Heard what?"

"About the balloon—"

The man choked, began coughing, and fell into a chair.
Wide awake now, Thaddeus shook him impatiently.

"Talk, man, talk! What about the balloon?"

"Wise's balloon is a failure. It caught in some trees and
collapsed while it was being towed toward the scene of the
battle at Bull Run. And the fighting is already under way!"

Thaddeus stared at him for a moment. Then, desperately,
he began flinging on his clothes.

"Hurry! Go find me some men. Meet me at the Mall."

"What are you going to do, Professor?"

"General McDowell needs a balloon. I am going to try to
get there in time with the *Enterprise*."

"But there are no orders for you. And the battle may end before you get there. And—"

"Do you think I will wait for orders while men are dying? Hurry, hurry!"

13

MR. LINCOLN VISITS GENERAL SCOTT

EVEN as he crossed the Potomac on the Long Bridge, Thaddeus knew with a gnawing certainty that he was too late. The battle would surely be decided before he could reach the scene. But he would not fail for lack of trying! Never had the *Enterprise* been prepared for action more rapidly.

Out past Fort Runyon he directed the course of the lurching craft, along a turnpike suddenly clogged with soldiers, civilians, carriages, everyone hastening somewhere, everyone getting in one another's way.

As they crossed the Loudoun & Hampshire Railroad he ground his teeth in despair, thinking how hopefully he had passed this way only four weeks before—and how pitifully the time had been wasted since then. If only Whipple and Bache had told him to go ahead with his plans! If only old General Scott had offered one word of encouragement! He could have been with McDowell's forces at the front long since, in a new balloon, sending word of every move the Rebels made.

But now . . .

Now the afternoon was slipping into evening, and rain was coming down in drenching torrents, and the battle was nearly twelve hours old already.

He pressed on, crying out urgently for speed from the twenty men loaned to him by Colonel William Small of the 26th Pennsylvania Infantry, not admitting defeat until he stumbled wearily into Falls Church and suddenly came face to face with the retreat.

From the direction of Centreville and Manassas soldiers were pouring toward him—limping, running, staggering. Some moved doggedly, turning now and again to look back through the darkness. Others panted and sobbed. In the faces of all Thaddeus could read disbelief and defeat.

McDowell had been defeated. The Confederates had won the first great battle of the war.

All through that wet and tragic night Thaddeus remained at Falls Church, waiting. Surely the Union would strike back. McDowell would regroup his men, mount a counterattack, somehow wring victory out of disaster. And this time, Thaddeus told himself grimly, he would be on the scene already.

But morning came and the terrible retreat continued. Through the wind and rain men hobbled, their eyes empty with horror. Wagons rumbled past with the bodies of the dead and dying. Still Thaddeus remained beside his balloon, waiting and hoping. A small force had been deployed as a rear guard in the area. Might McDowell be forming behind them, preparing to move up again?

In midafternoon a courier galloped up from the direction of Washington and gave the pickets orders to withdraw. Thaddeus conferred with the courier and the officer in charge of the guard, and returned woodenly to the little rise where his detail had waited all night and day with the *Enterprise*.

"It's over. There will be no counterattack. We must fall back to Fort Corcoran."

Not until eight o'clock that night did they get the *Enterprise* to Fort Corcoran, which guarded the Aqueduct Bridge upstream from Fort Runyon. The men of the detail had wanted to let the gas out of the balloon so they could move faster, but Thaddeus had refused. He could not bring himself to tell them why. Washington, the courier had told him, was in a state of panic. It was feared that General Beauregard and the victorious Southern forces would sweep into the capital itself, capture the seat of government, and end the war before it was well begun.

So even yet, Thaddeus reminded himself, he might be needed—and more urgently than ever. Not to aid in a great victory, but to reconnoiter the results of a crushing defeat.

He spent Tuesday at Fort Corcoran, stunned by the disorder everywhere about him, chafing at the stormy skies that kept him from going up in the balloon, listening to the rumors. Everywhere there were rumors. The Rebs were advancing . . . Washington was doomed . . . President Lincoln and the cabinet would flee the city.

On Wednesday morning the skies cleared at last, and Thaddeus knew the time had come to act.

This time a captive ascension with a telegraph wire would not be enough. He must rise high enough to see the countryside for miles around, he must move about in the upper currents freely to learn whether Beauregard was advancing, and where. He would make a free flight, then, and trust to the currents to set him down in Union territory.

He went up at 5:30 A.M. The *Enterprise* had been buffeted by the weather for four days now, but somehow the gas that had been pumped into the envelope in Washington still remained. Thaddeus let out ballast recklessly, found a westward current, and sailed directly toward the country occupied by the Confederates.

As the minutes passed into hours, his spirits began to lift a little.

The rumors were false. They had to be. He and he alone among all those on the Union side could see what was going on, and everything he saw convinced him that the Confederates were not advancing or even preparing to advance.

There was a considerable force encamped at Fairfax Court House. Beyond it, on the road to Centreville, he could make out two infantry regiments. Cavalry troops rode here and there. But nowhere could he see any great concentration of men, any pattern of forces deployed for an advance on Washington.

He must be sure. He would not return without certain knowledge. So hour after hour he kept vigil, rising three miles high to train his glasses on every corner of the horizon, dropping low to examine each suspicious sign of action.

At last, sure beyond doubt that Washington was not under any immediate threat, he prepared to land and rush the good news to the frightened capital. Up, up he went until he found a current that carried him swiftly to the Potomac. Then he began valving gas for a descent. With luck, he would land near Arlington Heights.

He was drifting downward when a sharp crack sounded below him. It was followed by another, and another. Something whistled past the rigging of the *Enterprise*. A thin cry rose to meet him.

"Show your colors!"

He peered over the side of the basket, and then drew his head back abruptly. Those were minié balls whistling past!

For a moment he couldn't understand it. Then he remembered. There had been rumors that the Confederates also had a balloon in action. The panicky troops at Arlington must believe they were being attacked by enemy aircraft.

"Show your colors!" The challenge echoed now from a dozen throats, and the firing increased.

"I have no colors!" he shouted back. "No colors! Let me land!"

Zinnnng!

Some other time, he thought as he tossed his remaining ballast overboard and soared up out of range, it would have been funny. Only three months ago he had been mistaken in South Carolina for a Union spy. Now he was under fire in Virginia as a Rebel. But it would not be so funny if he were shot down. . . .

The sound of firing grew fainter beneath him. Taking out his glasses, he swept the horizon. In the distance lay Alexandria, and below it a great area of plantation land. He tried vainly to remember which side controlled the country. Neither, perhaps. He would have to land between the lines and find his way back on foot.

And that, in the end, was how it worked out. He brought the *Enterprise* down on Mason's Plantation, two miles outside Federal lines, and hid himself as best he could from the danger of Rebel patrols until nightfall. A scouting party from the 31st New York Infantry found him there in the darkness, struggling to fold his damaged and now empty balloon, and helped him back to Alexandria. There he hastened to the telegraph office and flashed the news of his reconnaissance to the War Department.

The next day, newspapers all over the North carried the report. The capital was not in immediate danger. Thaddeus Lowe's free flight over enemy lines had established that Beauregard was not preparing an attack.

Bone-weary from his four days at the front, Thaddeus was sleeping late in his hotel room, just as he had the previous Sunday, when again there was a pounding on the door.

"Professor, wake up! President Lincoln sends his compliments and asks that you visit him this evening at the White House."

So for the third time Thaddeus went to the executive mansion to confer with the President of the United States. He was shocked by the deep lines of weariness and sorrow that etched Abraham Lincoln's face as he motioned his visitor to be seated at the big conference table. The disaster at Bull Run had left a heavy mark on the President.

But his courtesy had not changed. Gravely polite, he thanked Thaddeus in the name of the Union for his flight and the message of reassurance he had sent to the capital. He spoke only briefly of Sunday's stunning defeat, but a look almost of anger showed in his eyes when he added:

"If General McDowell had had more accurate information, the result might have been different. Such information could have come from your balloon, Professor."

Thaddeus nodded silently. Feeling the frustrations of the past weeks boiling up within him, he did not trust himself to speak.

In a low, controlled voice the President continued, speaking now of Thaddeus' own work. Joseph Henry must have told him how hard, and with what disappointments, Thaddeus had tried to win acceptance from the army, for he seemed to know it all—even the indifference General Scott had shown.

"Professor," he said at last, "I wish you would confer with General Scott again."

"Of course, sir. If he will admit me."

President Lincoln smiled. "Wait," he said, and reached for a pen. He scribbled something on a card and handed it over.

"Take this with you. And let me know the results of your meeting."

Thaddeus looked at the message. It read:

Will Lieut. Genl. Scott please see Professor Lowe once more about his balloon? A. Lincoln, July 25, 1861.

As he put it carefully away in his pocket, he saw the President rise. Now that the interview was ending, Abraham Lincoln seemed able for a moment to put aside the great burdens of his office. Smiling, he went to his desk, reached into a pigeonhole, and drew out a letter.

"From an admirer of yours in Philadelphia, Professor. It came soon after my war message to the Congress."

Thaddeus scanned the paper curiously.

"Dear Sir," it began. "Would it not be a grand idea to strike off hundreds of copies of your noble message and let Mr. Lowe ascend in his balloon and scatter them in Southern camps and all over the South. . . ."

He looked up eagerly. "If you wish it done, sir—"

Abraham Lincoln shook his head. "That time is past," he said. "We need you now with the armies. But it is an interesting idea. I will keep this letter among my papers."

Early the next morning Thaddeus hastened to General Scott's headquarters in the Winder Building across Seventeenth Street from the White House, and presented President Lincoln's card to an orderly. This time the general in chief would listen more carefully.

He was going over in his mind what he would say when the orderly returned.

"Sorry, sir, the general is engaged."

"But the President sent me. Did he see the card?"

The orderly surveyed him without expression. "The general is engaged," he repeated, handing back the card. "Perhaps if you come back later . . ."

Hiding his disappointment, Thaddeus left the building. For two hours he wandered aimlessly about Washington, too restless to do anything before the interview. Then he returned and offered the President's card to the orderly again.

There was another long wait before the soldier returned, his face as blank as before.

"The general is still engaged."

A dogged anger took control of Thaddeus. Without a word he left, walked the streets for another hour, and returned to wait a third time for his meeting with the general in chief.

This time the orderly's message was different.

"Sorry, sir. The general is at lunch."

Still without speaking, Thaddeus did an about-face, stepped out into the blazing July sun, and walked blindly into Lafayette Square. He sat there for nearly an hour before turning yet again to the Winder Building.

Would he spend the remainder of the war in this lunatic fashion, offering a card at a door, being refused, and returning to offer it again?

An expression of sympathy flashed across the face of the orderly as he handed the President's card back to Thaddeus for the fourth time.

"Sorry, sir. The general of the army is . . . ah . . . taking a nap."

So while the President of the United States waited for word of their conference, General Scott was dozing on a sofa! Thaddeus felt his face growing brick red. Wheeling, he stormed out, across the street, onto the lawn of the White House, and into the mansion itself.

Through crowds of people waiting for appointments he strode toward the President's office, shaking off a secretary who tried to intercept him. Outside the door of the office he was trying to explain his mission to a military aide when Abraham Lincoln himself looked out the door.

"Oh, Professor. Come in, come in."

Something about the sight of the President calmed him. Taking a tight rein on his indignation, he explained in a few sentences what had happened.

For a moment the President looked at him without expression. Then, surprisingly, he threw back his head and began to laugh.

"Come on," he said, still laughing, and reached for his stovepipe hat.

Puzzled, Thaddeus followed. Where were they going? What

had amused the President of the United States at such a time?
Even for him it was a hard task to keep up with Abraham
Lincoln's long-legged stride. Through the White House
grounds they walked, across Seventeenth Street, and—Thaddeus shook his head, hardly able to believe it—into the Winder Building.

As they flashed past General Scott's orderly, Thaddeus had
a fleeting instant in which to enjoy the look of blank amazement on the man's face. Then they were in the general's
office, and the old man was struggling to a sitting position on
his couch.

This, Thaddeus thought, was the man in top command of
the Union's military forces. The "Grand Old Man," he was
called, and he had been a great soldier in his prime. Now he
was old and gout-ridden and impatient of any new ideas. How
could . . .

"General," President Lincoln was saying pleasantly, "this
is my friend, Professor Lowe, who is organizing an aeronautics
corps for the army."

General Scott blinked at him sleepily and cleared his
throat with a great harrumph.

"I wish you would facilitate his work in every way."

The general was wide awake now, and sounds of agree-
ment were rumbling upward from his massive midsection.
He was smiling at Thaddeus as if he had never seen him but
had long hoped for the opportunity.

The President was smiling too. Nothing in his face hinted
that he had found it necessary to leave his office on a busy day
to see to it that his general in chief did what he had been
asked to do. It was as if the three of them had happened to
meet at a pleasant social affair.

What patience the man had! Thinking of it, and of his own
fierce, hot anger, Thaddeus suddenly wondered if that was
what made life endurable for the President. The patience to
hang onto a sense of proportion, of tolerance with the weak-

nesses of others . . . to laugh at annoyances, to keep calmly to the business at hand.

"Well, now, young man," the general was rumbling. "It seems to me I have heard great things about you."

Thaddeus looked at him, and found himself smiling as broadly as the President. After all, was it so outrageous that a seventy-five-year-old man needed a nap after lunch?

"Thank you, sir. And now, if you could spare me the time to explain my—"

"Of course, of course. Like nothing better!"

Still smiling, the President reached for his long fuzzy hat and left them to their plans.

14

AIR ARM OF THE UNION

A ROW of army tents hugged the crest of the hill, protected from the west by towering trees. In the slight hollow between the hill and the high land overlooking the Potomac, a new balloon of India silk tugged gently at its mooring ropes, its fresh varnish glittering in the sunlight.

Two men came out of the center tent and began walking toward the balloon. One of them, a tall, broad-shouldered man with coal-black hair and a heavy mustache, wore high riding boots, a dark coat and trousers, and a black slouch hat. Brilliant blue eyes scanned the sky as he spoke.

"A perfect day for aerial observations, General."

"Excellent." Brigadier General Fitz-John Porter, one of the most respected officers in the Army of the Potomac, was smiling broadly. He took off his plumed felt hat for a better look at the balloon.

"With your help, Professor Lowe, Jeb Stuart won't take us by surprise again."

"You can count on me, sir."

"I know I can. Now, let me explain the situation. General

William Smith, as you know, is about four miles upriver at the Chain Bridge. Two weeks ago he sent out a force toward Lewinsville. You will recall the results."

Thaddeus nodded grimly. Jeb Stuart, the daring Rebel cavalry commander, had attacked the party and driven it back, almost in the shadow of the Capitol. "Baldy" Smith had lost only eleven men, but the affair had been hailed in the South as a great victory, and there was no doubt it had been humiliating to the Union.

"Today it will be different." Fitz-John Porter's handsome face was coldly confident. "We must not be made ridiculous in the eyes of the world, Professor. General Smith is making a second reconnaissance on Lewinsville with more than double his first force. Five thousand men this time, and sixteen pieces of artillery."

"And I am to watch for the enemy."

"Exactly. My brigade here at Fort Corcoran is alerted. One word from you of a strong counterattack and we will move out in support."

"It is a great opportunity to be of service, sir. I hope you will find—"

"I know what I will find, Professor." General Porter smiled warmly. "I will find, as I have already found, that you are a man of courage, daring and resourcefulness. I expect great things of you."

He turned with a mock salute and strode back toward the fort. Flushing with pride, Thaddeus hurried to the balloon.

"Sergeant Eaton! Are we ready for an ascension?"

"Almost, sir." The sergeant in charge of the balloon detail had snapped smartly to attention. "Mooring cables have been made fast. Snatch blocks are attached to trees. Telescope and maps are in the basket. Anchoring ballast has been removed."

"Good work, Sergeant. Have the ascension ballast hooked to the car and deploy cable crews."

The preparations went like clockwork. Four lines of sol-

diers snaked out in different directions from the balloon, each
line holding a mooring cable that had been run through an
anchored pulley with a block attached for holding the cable
in place when desired. When the time came for ascension,
each line would pay out cable until the balloon reached its
desired height.

Thaddeus was taking his place in the car when a dull explosion sounded upriver.

BOOM!

He froze into position and listened.

BOOM! BOOM!

"Guns toward the Chain Bridge! Stand by your cables!"
Sergeant Eaton relayed the command, and the balloon
Union began rising slowly and majestically above Arlington
Heights. The guns were General Smith's, no doubt, but the
Aeronaut of the Army of the Potomac was determined to take
no chances.

The two months since he had seen General Scott had been
busy ones for Thaddeus. And despite the old general's luke-
warm assistance, they had begun on a note of discouragement.

He had been called on to make one more demonstration
flight in the aging *Enterprise,* and this time it had been a
failure. A windstorm came up before he was even ready for
the ascension, and he was forced to deflate the balloon rather
than have it wrecked.

Captain Whipple, already soured by the failures of James
Allen and John Wise, threw up his hands in disgust. Balloon
operations, he snapped, would be given up for good. But once
more Joseph Henry came to Thaddeus' support. It wasn't
fair, he insisted, to make judgments on a balloon which Thaddeus himself had said was too weak for use in strong winds.

So thanks once more to Professor Henry, his chance had
come. On August 2 he received a formal government order
for a new balloon of 25,000 cubic feet capacity, and hastened

back to Philadelphia to build it at his plant at Tenth and Chestnut streets.

By the morning of August 30 the *Union* was in the field—and by the afternoon of the same day Thaddeus had been fired on by the enemy. He had expected it, and he was ready. Coolly he remained aloft until he had completed his observations.

After that, matters moved smoothly. He was given a detail of thirty-four soldiers, a balloon camp was set up just below Fort Corcoran, and observation flights became a daily routine. The *Union* went up at all hours. General McDowell himself ascended with Thaddeus on September 5, and a few hours later the immaculate Fitz-John Porter took his own place in the basket.

From that day on, General Porter had been Thaddeus' strongest supporter. He arranged for an ascension by General George B. McClellan, who had taken command of the army after McDowell's failure at Bull Run, and the general they called "Little Mac" smiled with satisfaction at the results. Porter spent hours talking to McClellan and other generals about the value of balloons, and wrote long letters of encouragement to Thaddeus.

"I am desirous to see you prosper," he said in one of them, "and I think you are now on the road. I have recommended an increase of two balloons and moveable inflating apparatus. . . . I have no doubt of success. Strike now while the iron is hot."

Suddenly Thaddeus found himself one of the most talked-about men in the Union forces. Matthew Brady, the photographer, came to take pictures of him and his balloon. Artists from *Harper's Weekly* and *Leslie's* begged permission to go aloft with him. War correspondents clustered at his camp to learn what he had seen.

And Fitz-John Porter came out daily from Fort Corcoran to ask questions and spur him on.

"You really believe your portable generator will work, Professor?" he had asked only a few days ago. "They tell me John Wise designed one that was found to be completely impractical."

"General, I know my generator will work if I am ever allowed to build it. And with generators we can inflate balloons in the field. No more trips across a bridge from Washington."

Porter smiled at his confidence. "And you are just as sure, Professor, that you can direct artillery fire from your balloon? Such a thing has never been done before in American history."

"Of course I can, sir. Either by telegraph or by flag signals. From the air it is easy to see whether the batteries are firing over or under their targets, or to the right or left. Corrections will be simple enough."

"Well, Professor, I have arranged a test for you. General Smith will be directing artillery fire on Falls Church tomorrow. You will observe from here."

And it had worked! First by telegraph and then by flag signals, Thaddeus reported firing errors. More than three miles away, Baldy Smith's men at Chain Bridge made their corrections. The generals, all of them, had been delighted.

The booming of the guns faded to echoes as the *Union* rose over Arlington Heights, and Thaddeus glued his eye to his telescope. Today's job was to guard General Smith's reconnaissance to Lewinsville, and Fitz-John Porter was counting on him.

As he had suspected, the guns were those of General Smith. Looking toward Chain Bridge, Thaddeus could see the flash of Union bayonets glistening in the sun as the force marched toward Lewinsville. He signaled the news to Sergeant Eaton and settled down to his vigil.

As he watched, he wondered. Would the two additional balloons recommended by General Porter be approved, and the generators too? It had been ten days now since Porter had asked him to draw up a statement of what the new equipment would cost. Had the proposal been turned down?

Three balloons. The very thought filled him with excitement. Even if one were held in reserve, that would mean two ready for constant use. If they would let him hire another aeronaut, there could be *two* balloon camps guarding the troops along the Potomac.

He must not get too hopeful, he warned himself. Already he had achieved more than had seemed possible a short while ago. And right now the important thing was to watch out for Jeb Stuart.

It was the watching that counted.

The Confederate cavalrymen did not appear. Hour after hour Thaddeus scanned the distance, watching for some sign that the enemy was trying to cut General Smith's men off, but it did not come. Satisfied at last, he gave the signal and was hauled down.

He was seated beside the balloon, writing a report to General Porter, when an orderly approached.

"Professor Lowe? I have a message for you from General Montgomery Meigs of the Quartermaster Corps."

Thaddeus reached eagerly for the dispatch.

SIR: Upon recommendation of Major General McClellan, the Secretary of War has directed that four additional balloons be at once constructed, under your direction, together with such inflating apparatus as may be necessary for them and the one now in use. It is desirable that they may be completed with the least possible delay.

Thaddeus' whoops of joy brought Sergeant Eaton running.

"Not just two more balloons, but *four!* And portable generators for all of them. Why, with five balloons I can organize an entire air corps!"

"Believe me, Father, we will make history. Tomorrow I want you to see my new balloons."

Thaddeus' home in Philadelphia was a festive place that

late October night in 1861. Work on the balloons was almost completed. Clovis Lowe had arrived that afternoon for a visit, and Leontine and the children had insisted on a celebration.

From the beginning, Clovis had followed his son's balloon work with deep interest and excitement. Time after time he had left his home in New Hampshire to watch and help. And since the war began, he had been more eager than ever to see what Thaddeus was doing. Tonight he had insisted on hearing everything that had happened.

While the children listened wide-eyed, Thaddeus told his story, leaving out nothing.

"But what's this I heard about a runaway balloon, son? You haven't mentioned that."

"I'm just getting to it, Father. That happened the middle of this month. General Smith was so set on having more observations at Lewinsville that he couldn't wait for the new balloons. He sent word for me to come back to Washington and join him with the *Union*."

"And you did?"

Thaddeus smiled ruefully. "Not quite. Oh, how sick I am of inflating balloons in Washington and then towing them out to the field. With my generator—"

"Yes, yes, of course. But what happened?"

"Well, it was nine o'clock at night when we set out from Washington. Dark as pitch, and trees, telegraph wires and flag ropes everywhere to cause us trouble. We had to go by way of Georgetown and the Chain Bridge. Sometimes we had to stop and cut down trees to clear a way. We got to the bridge at three in the morning, and it was jammed with cavalry and artillery crossing over to Virginia."

Clovis Lowe whistled in dismay. "What did you do? Wait?"

"Wait when you've been ordered to join Baldy Smith?" Thaddeus laughed. "Not on your life, Father. There are big trestles over the bridge, you know. Well, my men climbed inches wide—nearly a hundred feet above the bed of the river."

"And where were you?"

"In the balloon car above them, directing the management of the ropes. It was quite a scene. A dark, stormy night, the balloon high in the air, your humble servant leaning out of the bag and shouting, the ground crew crawling along the top of the bridge, a column of artillery beneath them, and the river thundering over the rocks below."

"Thaddeus! You never told me." Leontine's face was pale with alarm.

"All in the day's work, my dear," Thaddeus joked. Then he sobered. "But after all that trouble, and after more hours of struggling through the Virginia countryside toward Lewinsville, we failed. A terrible storm came up. I got out of the balloon and we lashed it to some stumps in the field. But the storm got so fierce it broke the ropes."

"And the *Union?* What happened to the *Union?*"

"Why, it sailed off in the direction of Baltimore. It finally landed in Delaware and I've had all sorts of trouble getting it back. But we got it. It's at the assembly building now, being repaired."

"Ah, yes, the assembly building." Clovis Lowe's eyes were wistful. "I can hardly wait to see the work in progress, Thaddeus." He paused, looking down at his feet. "Son," he said at last, "I want to be of some help in this great enterprise. That's really why I came. Do you think you can use me?"

Thaddeus felt a lump in his throat. That his own father would offer to help!

"Thank you, sir. You have no idea how hard I have struggled to find good men. They are counting on me to hire the aeronauts and the assistants to operate these balloons, you know. I must organize and build an entire aeronautics corps from nothing—and you know how few men there are to choose from."

"That's just what I mean, son. Am I hired?"

For a moment Thaddeus hesitated, thinking of the danger and of his father's age. Then, seeing the look in the older man's eyes, he broke into a smile.

"You're hired, Father. But don't forget. When I make you the ground assistant in charge of one of my balloon camps, you'll have to take orders from your own son!"

Down the Potomac River, past Alexandria, and on toward Budd's Ferry, Maryland, moved a strange craft, towed by the naval tug *Coeur de Lion.*

She was a shallow-draft vessel, a converted lighter by the look of her, with a completely flat deck more than a hundred feet long. A great box on wheels, big as an army wagon, lay on her bow and several barrels adorned her stern. Amidships lay a mass of silk, covered with a network of cords.

Union lookouts along the river looked at her and rubbed their eyes. The name painted on her hull—*G. W. Parke Custis* —meant nothing to them. What could she be?

From his position on the deck of the tug, Thaddeus Lowe saw the knots of curious soldiers and grinned happily. They might well wonder what that craft was, for the world had never seen one just like her before. The first aircraft carrier in history!

The *Custis* had indeed been a lighter, a coal barge in fact, when Thaddeus first got his hands on her. Secretary of the Navy Gideon Welles had let him have the eight-year-old boat, and he had converted her lovingly into a carrier.

That mass of silk on her deck was the fine new balloon *Constitution,* bound for General Joe Hooker's command far downriver from Washington. Looking at the folded envelope, Thaddeus could see part of the decoration painted on it, a tremendous likeness of George Washington.

And that big box on the bow—that was his first portable generator, a device of his own invention. Inside the box was a tank. You put iron filings into it, spread them evenly, covered them with water, and poured in sulphuric acid through a tube. A gas came off. You passed this gas through a cooler and a purifier and you had hydrogen for inflating your balloon.

It was a big, heavy affair—four horses were needed to pull it—but it changed the whole practice of military ballooning. Now, for the first time, envelopes could be inflated in the field.

And now, with aircraft carrier and generators, Thaddeus was ready to put the newly born aeronautics corps into action. It was a moment he had dreamed of for weeks, planning, organizing, hiring men, fighting for money and supplies, sometimes despairing that it would ever become real.

But real it was! Tomorrow he would inflate the *Constitution* from the deck of the *Custis* and go up for an observation flight himself. Then the balloon and generator would be sent ashore under the care of William Paullin, one of the newly hired aeronauts. Paullin knew how to handle balloons. Thaddeus could still remember calling on him for help in Philadelphia, that distant day when he had put on an aerial show for the visiting Japanese.

And, with Paullin holding down the left flank of the Union line, Thaddeus would steam off with his aircraft carrier to place other balloons in position. Next, he thought, would be . . .

"Professor!"

"Yes, Captain Whittlesey?"

The skipper of the *Coeur de Lion* was pointing through the haze. "There's Mattawoman Creek ahead. A good place to drop anchor. General Hooker's headquarters are at Posey's House, not far from here."

"Very well, Captain."

Even before the anchor was dropped, a small boat had put

out from the mouth of the creek and Thaddeus heard someone shout his name.

"Professor Lowe! Remember me?"

"Of course. War correspondent for the New York *Herald,*
aren't you?"

The reporter flushed with pleasure at being recognized.
"That's right, sir. And what do you have here?"

"Why, news for your paper. The first balloon expedition by
water ever attempted. And we make an ascension tomorrow."

"May I go up with you?"

"Of course, if General Hooker approves. Right now I must
send him a message."

"I'm going toward Posey's House myself. Be glad to guide
your messenger."

"Fine. Just a moment." And Thaddeus sat down to write
his dispatch to General Joseph Hooker:

> Sir: In obedience to orders of Major General McClellan,
> I have come to this place for the purpose of making an aero-
> nautic observation. . . .

As 1861 drew to a close, Thaddeus pushed himself relent-
lessly.

He was everywhere at once—working in the big armory at
Washington which had become storage and repair headquarters for the balloons, hastening by horseback or aircraft
carrier to establish new balloon camps, rushing back to Philadelphia for some bit of badly needed equipment, making
constant observation flights of his own.

And week by week the Aeronautics Corps became a reality.

In mid November, the dashing General McClellan held a
grand review of the Army of the Potomac at Bailey's Cross
Roads—and while the massed thousands of troops marched,
Thaddeus was a few miles away in the *Intrepid,* viewing the
enemy encampments from the air and putting to rest a report
that the Rebels were about to advance.

A few days later he was sailing his aircraft carrier past the Rebel batteries along the lower Potomac and into Chesapeake Bay, delivering the balloon *Washington* and an aeronaut, James Starkweather, to Fortress Monroe for shipment to Port Royal, South Carolina.

December found him building two more balloons and perfecting his organization along the Potomac River. Now there were three balloon camps acting as eyes for McClellan's great army—one with General Hooker on the left flank at Budd's Ferry, a second with General Stone on the right flank at Edwards Ferry, and a third with General Porter in the center of the line opposite Washington.

Busy as he was with his own work, Thaddeus had little time at first to listen to the constant arguments in the capital about the conduct of the war. But as the new year began, the bickering grew too loud for him to ignore.

It centered around General George McClellan, the man who had been hailed as the hope of the Union when he first arrived in Washington. Everyone had cheered him. In November he had succeeded old Winfield Scott as general in chief of the armies. But now the politicians who thronged the capital were turning against him.

For months, they said, he had drilled the Army of the Potomac without advancing against the Confederates. Was he afraid to fight?

The complaints grew louder. Even President Lincoln, it was said, was growing restless. Once, while Little Mac was lying ill, the President was quoted as saying that if General McClellan didn't plan to use his army, he would like to borrow it for a while. Around the Capitol, they said Lincoln had found out what ailed the general: he suffered from the slows.

McClellan recovered from his illness and calmly went on drilling his troops, while the complaints in the capital grew louder. Toward the end of January, President Lincoln issued an order that had the whole city talking. The Army of the

Potomac was publicly directed to move out and recapture Manassas on or before February 22.

Fitz-John Porter, who had discussed the complaints with Thaddeus a time or two at the balloon camp near his head-quarters, was hotly indignant.

"Politicians know nothing about war, Professor," he said. "They think they can win battles by passing a bill, or by issuing Presidential orders that serve only to alert the enemy. General McClellan knows what he is doing. This army was a broken mob when he took command. Look at it now!"

It was true, Thaddeus thought. The Army of the Potomac had become a magnificently disciplined fighting force. The soldiers worshiped Little Mac. There was no doubt in *their* minds that he would lead them to victory when the time came.

February 22 passed and the Army of the Potomac remained in its winter quarters. It was said that McClellan had per-suaded the President to give him more time, that he had a plan to surprise the Southern forces. No one knew exactly what the plan was, but there was much talk of a flanking move to get between the Rebels and their capital at Rich-mond.

But there were problems closer at hand to claim Thaddeus' attention. General McClellan, as general in chief of the Union armies, had ordered him to send a balloon train to Cairo, Illinois, to be used in the advance down the Mississippi River. And even as he worked out plans to send one of his aeronauts, John Steiner, to Cairo with the balloon *Eagle*, another matter came up.

This one was unpleasant. John LaMountain, who had made a number of ascents from land and water at Fortress Monroe for General Ben Butler, had wandered up to Washington in search of work. While he didn't like the man, Thaddeus told himself, it was no concern of his. But when LaMountain began trying to get his hands onto the balloons Thaddeus had worked so hard to produce, the sparks began to fly.

Then LaMountain began to fight dirty. He accused Thaddeus of cheating the government, of disobeying orders, of interfering with matters that did not concern him. This was too much. Thaddeus carried the fight all the way to General McClellan's headquarters, where it promptly ended with LaMountain being told his services were no longer needed.

Thaddeus was greatly relieved when it was over. He hated this petty in-fighting, whether it was between generals or between aeronauts. There was a war to be fought. Everyone should work together.

And now, as February drew toward an end, a stir of anticipation began to sweep the Army of the Potomac from one end to the other. Something was in the air. McClellan was ready to make his move at last.

As the excitement increased, Thaddeus was given a new assignment. General Heintzelman, commanding the troops around Alexandria, wanted a balloon camp set up near George Washington's old home at Mount Vernon to watch for any sign of enemy movements in the area.

Wondering what it was all about, Thaddeus rushed a balloon to a little crossroads known as Pohick Church and began making daily ascents. There could be no doubt, he felt, that something big was brewing.

General Heintzelman went up with him on March 6, and what they saw convinced them that the Rebels were planning a vast withdrawal—not only from Manassas, but from the positions they had held along the lower reaches of the Potomac. One look at the general's face told Thaddeus how important it was.

The news was flashed to McClellan. Almost immediately, Thaddeus got fresh orders. He must get another balloon ready at once for an advance.

He hastened back to Washington, and suddenly found himself in the middle of one of the wildest and most confused days the capital had ever experienced.

Part of what happened that strange day he learned from a white-faced and angry Fitz-John Porter. Part he heard from his newspaper friends. And part he observed himself. It was a remarkable story.

President Lincoln had invited McClellan to breakfast and told him he had been accused of treason!

There was a sharp irony about it. When Little Mac wasn't ready to fight, his critics had hinted it was because he wanted to help the South. Now that he was about to advance, they said he wanted to leave the capital helpless before an enemy attack.

Abraham Lincoln had hastened to add that he himself did not believe the charges. But General McClellan, almost speechless with outrage, had insisted that his name be cleared. Let his division commanders meet and discuss his campaign plan among themselves, he said. He would not be present. They could vote on whether the plan was a good one.

The President agreed. The division commanders met and approved the plan. All seemed to be well. And then, without even discussing it with McClellan, President Lincoln suddenly issued an order changing the whole organization of the Army of the Potomac. He divided it into four corps—and he named the corps commanders himself.

There had been other excitement on this eventful day. News swept the capital that a fearful new kind of Rebel warship, the *Virginia,* had sunk two Union ships in Chesapeake Bay and might even now be advancing up the Potomac to the capital.

The *Virginia* was the former Union ship *Merrimac*. The Confederacy had taken it and armored it in iron. It was said to be invincible. It might win the war single-handed. Panic swept the capital again.

Confused, uneasy, and angry at the treatment of a general

he respected, Thaddeus tried to put it all out of his mind and get his work done at the Armory. The balloon at Edwards Ferry must be brought back for the advance toward Manassas. Generators must be made ready. Work details must be arranged.

Somehow he got through the day. The next day there was a fresh deluge of news.

The *Virginia* was not invincible after all. It had been engaged by the *Monitor,* a Union ironclad built by John Ericcson, and driven back. . . .

The Rebels had definitely abandoned Manassas. . . .

McClellan had ordered the Army of the Potomac to move. . . .

The balloon *Intrepid* must be at Fairfax Court House next morning without fail. . . .

Somehow, in all the hurry and excitement, he made it. On March 10, in a driving rain, the Army of the Potomac marched out from its encampments along the river and advanced on Manassas. Thaddeus and the balloon *Intrepid* advanced with it.

General McClellan established his headquarters at Fairfax Court House, with Thaddeus nearby to provide eyes for him. The army occupied Centreville and Manassas on the eleventh.

But after all the stir, it was an empty victory. The Confederates had gone. And now that they had fallen back, what of McClellan's hotly debated plan to get between them and Richmond? Was it too late?

Rumors were flying wildly as Thaddeus continued his observations on March 12. Little Mac had been removed from command . . . no, he had merely lost his title of general in chief . . . he was still in command of the Army of the Potomac . . . the plans for the great attack were all being changed. . . .

Then, as if by magic, everyone was talking about "the Peninsula." What it all meant no one was sure, but something was in the wind involving the Army of the Potomac and "the Peninsula."

While he wondered what it meant, Thaddeus got fresh orders. A balloon must be sent at once to Fortress Monroe at the foot of Chesapeake Bay. Its mission: to watch for any sign of the Rebel ironclad *Virginia,* and to scan the long finger of land between the York and the James rivers. . . .

The Peninsula! Eyes hot with excitement, Thaddeus began to guess what was afoot.

While couriers rushed madly in and out of McClellan's headquarters at Fairfax Court House, Thaddeus dashed off orders to Eben Seaver, the aeronaut at Budd's Ferry. Seaver must take the balloon *Constitution* to Fortress Monroe at once. The whole army would be following.

The fighting was about to begin in earnest.

15

THE PENINSULA

IT HAD been dark between the scattered campfires, dark and muddy and hopelessly confused. But now a pale April sun was rising over the frowning walls of Fortress Monroe in the distance. Thaddeus lengthened his stride. Sergeant Eaton and the balloon train should be just over there, beyond the ruins of that house.

"Ah, there you are, Sergeant. Ready to move out?"

Charles Eaton saluted briskly. "Just about, Professor. I'm waiting for one more carboy of acid from the balloon boat. It ought to be here any minute."

"You'll have time. Our wagons are ordered to fall in at the rear of General Porter's line. Just be sure we have everything."

"Right, sir." The big sergeant's face relaxed into a grin. "A little sunlight will be a friendly thing, won't it?"

Thaddeus leaned down to brush a great chunk of mud off his boot. "It will indeed."

The rains had been endless, he thought as he looked across the mudholes of Hampton toward Old Point Comfort and the fort. On this storm-swept peninsula, it seemed more a miracle than ever that the entire Army of the Potomac with all its equipment had traveled two hundred miles by water in barely more than two weeks.

But somehow McClellan had managed it, and without the loss of a man. Down the Potomac from Washington and Alexandria and into the choppy waters of Chesapeake Bay the army had come in an endless parade—a fleet of four hundred boats carrying nearly 100,000 men, along with wagons, pontoon bridges, horses, mules, gun batteries.

Down to the very foot of the bay they had come, to where the long finger of land thrusting out between the York and James rivers had appeared, with Fortress Monroe at its very tip.

The Peninsula. The road to Richmond.

The first troops had landed during a great storm and pitched their tents under Monroe's guns or amid the mud of nearby Hampton. Then the storm died away and cold, dreary rains took its place. It had been raining when the balloon boat *Custis* arrived.

Thaddeus had not been dry since then. There had scarcely been time to change his clothes. It was raining when he hastened to the fort to find Eben Seaver and get a report of his ascensions in the *Constitution*. It rained all the time he listened to Seaver's bitter complaints of the confusion and red tape that hampered his work. It rained while he directed the unloading of the *Custis*. And it was still raining when he found Fitz-John Porter yesterday and discussed plans for the advance up the Peninsula.

Yes, a little sunshine would be friendly. Otherwise, how could this great army march through the swamps and marshes of the Peninsula?

General Porter had explained the plan to him after the staff officers had met with General McClellan.

"As you know, the army is divided into four corps now."

Porter's face reflected his anger at the memory of President Lincoln's order. "The First Corps, under McDowell, has not yet arrived. We start without him. Heintzelman's Third Corps will be on the right, with my division in the lead. Keyes' Fourth Corps will be on the left. Sumner and the Second Corps will be in support."

"I understand."

"Now about yourself. I have asked for you, Professor. Our side of the line moves directly on Yorktown, twenty-five miles from here, and we will need you to act as our eyes when we get there."

"Yes, sir. Any hope of a break in the weather?"

"Our weathermen believe the day will be clear tomorrow. But your train is heavy. We can't have your wagons tearing up the roads ahead of my men—the guns will do enough of that. Fall in behind our column, and mind you don't lose a wagon in the mud!"

Well, the weathermen had been right after all. The faint overcast was disappearing now as the sun rose higher. And now Hampton was echoing to shouts and whistles, the neighing of horses, the hoarse brays of army mules. Off in the distance Thaddeus could see the first units of Porter's command already beginning the march.

Sergeant Eaton saw the movement too, stirred restlessly, and eyed the four army wagons and two gas generators that made up the balloon train.

"About ready, Professor."

"About ready, Sergeant. On to Richmond!"

But Richmond was seventy miles up the Peninsula from Fortress Monroe, and that first day Porter's division did not even reach Yorktown. The men marched out briskly enough, but there were constant delays before the morning was well begun. Wagons mired down. Logs that had been felled across the muddy roads had to be moved. The army maps showed

roads that did not exist, and men had to wait for hours while
new routes were worked out.

Riding at the end of the column with his balloon train,
Thaddeus began to notice bits of army clothing all along the
line of march. In the bright sunshine, the soldiers were throwing away their overcoats and blankets to lighten their loads.
Some had even discarded their packs, extra pairs of shoes,
parade uniforms.

Sergeant Eaton was disturbed at the waste. "They think
they'll be in Richmond next week," he said hotly. "They
think they won't need a change of clothes before the war is
over. They'll be sorry."

The division camped along the line of march that night,
and the rains began again. During the night a courier from
Fortress Monroe galloped into camp. Among his dispatches
was a message to Thaddeus from Eben Seaver.

Thaddeus opened it uneasily. He had talked sternly to his
angry assistant before he left Hampton. Seaver had done good
work at Fortress Monroe before the army reached the Peninsula, but now he could do nothing but complain. Why hadn't
he been given a commission as major? Where was his pay?
Why wouldn't the officers give him more cooperation?

There was reason enough for complaint, Thaddeus knew,
but he tried to explain that the work must go on anyhow.
True, Seaver had not been made an officer—neither had
Thaddeus. Every aeronaut in the Balloon Corps was still a
civilian. And when pay was late in coming, or when trouble
arose with officers who didn't understand balloon problems,
of course it was annoying. You simply had to make the best
of it.

"Forget your own troubles," Thaddeus had told him.
"Your job is to keep that balloon in the air as much as possible. I will not have a man in my corps who doesn't stick to
his job. William Paullin is a good man, but he was neglecting
his work to make money on the side. I let him go and hired

James Allen. Think about that, Seaver. I expect complete devotion to their jobs from all my men."

They were hard words, but Thaddeus felt they were necessary. And now, looking at Seaver's letter, he wondered if they had been enough. The balloon was ready to ascend, Seaver wrote, but he couldn't get orders to take it up.

"I wish very much this balloon was where you are," he complained. "Your authority accomplishes more in five minutes than another person could in a day."

Thaddeus smiled wearily. In a way it was true. Lacking the authority that went with an army commission, he had made his own by his attitude. Men treated him like a field officer because he acted as if he expected them to. Why couldn't Seaver do the same?

He went to sleep thinking that he must discuss this matter with James Allen while his new aeronaut was fresh on the job. Let men know you put a high value on yourself, that was the thing. . . .

They were up early the next morning, and the march began again. A little after noon the long line came to a halt. Thaddeus rode ahead to find what had happened.

Tents were already going up on the damp ground when he found General Porter.

"Ah, Professor. I was about to send for you. That river ahead of us is the Warwick, and Yorktown lies just beyond it. My scouts tell me the town is heavily fortified. I want your balloon up as soon as possible. We have work to do—"

Abruptly, the general pulled off his hat and flung it angrily to the ground. "If Washington will only let us do it, that is."

"Has something happened, General?"

"It has. I have just learned from General McClellan that President Lincoln has countermanded McDowell's orders. The First Corps will not join us for this campaign. It is being held near Washington in case of an attack on the capital. And we have already been denied the use of General Wool's troops at Fortress Monroe."

Eben Seaver should be here, Thaddeus thought as he returned to the balloon train. Perhaps he would discover that even generals must learn to live with frustrations in war.

All through the afternoon he worked with Sergeant Eaton, James Allen and the ground crew, setting up a balloon camp and preparing for an ascension. Once they were interrupted by an outburst of firing from the direction of Yorktown, and Thaddeus realized with a start that the Peninsular Campaign had begun in earnest.

By 5:30 the balloon was ready to be taken up.

"Stand by your cables!"

As the basket rose high over the Union encampment, a volley of shots rang out from the rifle pits across the river. Thaddeus scarcely noticed. Suddenly he was filled with an overpowering sense of being in the presence of history.

Here, in this very area, Cornwallis had surrendered to Washington less than a hundred years ago—and now the nation so nobly born was torn in two. Was the dream of the Founding Fathers to die near the spot where it had begun?

Curiously he looked across the sluggish river to the little town so rich in history. Yorktown was protected by a massive line of earthworks from which great guns ominously pointed their snub noses in Thaddeus' direction. Nearby, on his right, ran the broad York River, and on its far side opposite Yorktown stood the fortifications of Gloucester. Taking this stronghold would be no overnight task.

He stayed up an hour or so, sketching, making notes, straining his eyes in the failing light. Then he gave the signal to be lowered.

General Porter listened to his report with intense interest.

"It is what I expected. Professor, from this day I want your balloon in the air at every opportunity. I want to know everything that can be learned about the enemy—his strength, his movements, his weak points, any sign of arrivals or withdrawals, the number of his campfires—"

"I understand, General."

He ate supper in darkness, conferred with his assistants, and snatched a few hours of uneasy sleep. By three in the morning he was riding the breezes a thousand feet above the Union army, studying the number and disposition of campfires.

A thickening fog drove him down two hours later. After a quick breakfast he went to General Porter's headquarters to report.

He was leaving when a thought occurred to him.

"Sir, may I invite you to go up with me and see the enemy's works for yourself?"

Fitz-John Porter was already rising from his camp chair.

"Let's go, Professor."

For nearly two hours Thaddeus and the general remained at a height of one thousand feet, less than a mile from the nearest emplacements of the enemy. Guns roared at them constantly. Once a ball whistled by so closely they could hear it, and General Porter grunted.

"We make good target practice for the Rebs. Too bad we must leave them. It is time for me to go down."

Thaddeus spent almost all day in the air. After General Porter had descended and called a council of field-grade officers, draftsmen were sent up to make maps. Later the Count de Paris, pretender to the throne of France and a volunteer aide on McClellan's staff, asked to go up. When he descended, General Daniel Butterfield was waiting his turn.

Finally, late in the day, Thaddeus gave Sergeant Eaton the signal to anchor the balloon for the night. As the work was being done, James Allen emerged from the twilight.

"An order from General McClellan, Professor. The Fourth Corps needs a balloon for the left side of the line of march.

You are to deliver one at Warwick Court House as soon as possible."

Thaddeus considered. "It will take a day or two at least. I'll send a messenger back to Hampton tonight with orders to get a balloon and generator ready to move. Can you take my place here?"

Allen smiled happily. "I've just been waiting to show you what I can do, sir."

"Good. Then tomorrow I'll give you a chance to learn our routine and take the balloon up yourself. Tuesday, if all goes well, I'll leave you in charge and go for the other balloon."

And that was how it worked out. James Allen, a skilled balloonist on his own, had carefully observed the strict routines Thaddeus had set up for inflating, anchoring, and all the other balloon functions, and on Monday he proved he could handle the balloon well. Thaddeus spent much of the day struggling through the mass of paperwork involved in getting the mules and wagons he needed.

On Tuesday he returned to Hampton, where the reserve balloon equipment was kept, and by nightfall he had the details worked out. The mules had been assigned. The wagons were ready. Thaddeus was tired out but satisfied with his work.

After a hot supper at the fort he returned to Hampton and settled down to write a letter to his wife. Things were going well, he told her. Soon he would be able to take things easier and leave more of the work to his assistants.

"Kiss the little ones for me," he added, thinking nostalgically of his happy family back in Philadelphia. Then he stretched out on a cot and went to sleep.

All day Wednesday and Thursday he worked setting up the new balloon camp. The trip with the wagon train from Hampton to Warwick was unbelievably hard. Wagons mired down every few yards in the soggy wilderness of mud. Even after they arrived, there were a hundred details to attend to before he was satisfied with the new camp.

It was late in the day when the job was done at last. Thaddeus reported to General Keyes, the corps commander, and promised to send James Allen over early in the morning to make an ascent. Then he set out in the darkness to return to the balloon camp opposite Yorktown.

He was dozing in the saddle hours later when a low whistle brought him bolt upright, cold with alarm.

There was something wrong about that whistle. . . .

In a moment his sleepiness vanished. Looking about him through the heavy shadows, he was more sure than ever that something was wrong. Over there—there was where the balloon camp should be. But it wasn't. What was that faint glimmer of light ahead?

The whistle sounded again and a low voice drifted through the darkness to him.

"High time you got here, soldier. I'm due to be back in Yorktown asleep right now."

With infinite caution Thaddeus dismounted, turned his horse, and led it silently back in the direction he had come. His face was beaded with cold perspiration. A few more steps and he would have blundered directly into a Rebel outpost!

He learned why when he rode into the camp of one of Porter's regiments a few minutes later. There had been a shift in the lines while he was absent. The balloon camp had been moved.

"Lucky for you that you heard that whistle," the sentry told him cheerfully after hearing his story. "They tell me those Rebel prisons aren't very comfortable. You going to set out in the dark again?"

"Not on your life, soldier. I'm staying right here with you the rest of the night."

He was up at daybreak, sharing a pot of hot coffee with a

little group of enlisted men at a campfire. Then he set out afresh to find the balloon camp.

The sentry had given him easy directions for reaching it. He was nearing the spot when a sound of shouting in the distance made him look up.

Well, there was his destination at last. The balloon was rising even now. James Allen was on the job—

But wait!

The balloon was still rising.

Higher and higher it went. Then it wavered and began to move in the direction of Yorktown.

A free flight! Could Allen be so foolhardy as to risk flying the balloon directly over the enemy lines? What in the . . .

The big bag surged back in his direction. And now, with the sun bright behind him, he could make out the figure in the basket.

It wasn't Allen at all. It was . . . it was . . . General Fitz-John Porter!

And as Thaddeus stared dumbfounded and the sound of shouting grew louder, General Porter and the balloon began drifting back toward the bristling ramparts of Yorktown.

16

YORKTOWN

FOR a fraction of a second Thaddeus was too startled to move. Then he was off his horse, sprinting in the direction of the balloon, and shouting hoarsely.

"Ballast, General! Throw off ballast!"

It was no use, of course. Fitz-John Porter could not possibly hear him. In another minute the balloon would be directly over Yorktown, the rifles would find their target, and one of the top generals of the Army of the Potomac would be lost to the Union.

Sick at heart, he stumbled through the gathering crowd and reached the center of the balloon camp.

"Quick! A telescope!"

He felt it thrust into his hands. Numbly he put it to his eye—and a moment later he was weak with relief.

General Porter was throwing off ballast.

The balloon shot upward. Thaddeus followed it with the glass, losing it once and then finding it again well out of range of enemy bullets. But what, he asked himself, was the general doing now?

Could he actually be . . . ?

He was.

At the look of wonder on Thaddeus' face as he took the telescope down, the crowd around him grew silent. Sergeant Eaton spoke first.

"What is it, sir? What's the matter?"

Thaddeus shook his head weakly. "It's all right. The general is out of range of Rebel fire for the moment. He is . . . he is observing and taking notes."

A delighted burst of laughter shook the crowd. Who but the dashing General Porter, finding himself in a runaway balloon above the enemy, would calmly reach for a pencil and begin recording what he saw?

But while the others cheered, Thaddeus was already cold with apprehension, wondering what would happen next. General Porter was a veteran at balloon ascensions, but he had always been an observer before. And he had never been up for a free flight. Would he know what to do when the opportunity came?

As Thaddeus resumed his watch, the situation changed again. The wind had altered its course, and now the balloon came floating back toward the Union lines. He saw General Porter put down his note pad, look calmly about him, and reach for the valve rope.

"Open the valve!" someone was shouting.

"Never mind," Thaddeus cried. "He knows."

With a sudden puff, the great envelope collapsed. General Porter was taking no chances of drifting back a second time—he had let all the gas escape. The silk swooshed upward, flattening itself against the cords, and formed a parachute. And Fitz-John Porter drifted triumphantly down, landing with a smash on top of a small tent.

A period of vast confusion followed. The tent collapsed. The silk of the balloon fell billowing on top of the general.

A squad of cavalry galloped to the scene, and hundreds of onlookers, Thaddeus among them, raced to follow.

The general was on his feet, laughing heartily, when Thaddeus reached the spot. A staff officer was pounding him on the back.

". . . first man I ever knew who was arrested by a shelter tent!"

Porter's eye found Thaddeus, and he smiled ruefully.

"Ah, Professor. I borrowed your balloon."

But for all the joking and rejoicing, it had been a serious accident and Thaddeus was determined to get to the bottom of it. What had happened?

James Allen, his honest face white with embarrassment and shame, explained.

"It was my fault, sir. I was nervous. The general was in a hurry to ascend. Instead of the four mooring cables you usually use, I settled for only one. And look here."

They were back at the balloon camp now, and Allen was holding out the end of a rope. Acid had eaten it almost through.

"Some of the vitriol must have spilled on it. It snapped when we let it out to its full length. Believe me, Professor, I have learned my lesson."

Seeing his assistant's distress, Thaddeus knew any further punishment would be unnecessary. And as they talked, he began to understand how James Allen could have let the general's impatience lead him to such carelessness.

What had happened during Thaddeus' absence had been enough to make anyone nervous and uncertain. Rumors of spies bent on destroying the balloon had swept through the camp. A lame peddler had been halted by Sergeant Eaton just as he was in the act of lighting his pipe in the gas-filled atmosphere near the balloon—an act that could have caused an explosion wrecking the balloon in a moment. And not only that, but the morning before a patrol had captured a score of Rebels near the balloon camp, all of them armed with high-powered rifles.

As he listened, Thaddeus grew thoughtful.

"It sounds like part of an organized plan to destroy the balloon, James. Too bad that peddler has disappeared. I suspect he knew exactly what he was doing. If we had captured him, we might have learned the whole plot."

But the peddler was gone, and it would not be until years later that Thaddeus learned his suspicions had been true. After the war was over, the peddler himself told the whole story to a newspaper reporter.

The defenders of Yorktown, he said, had been determined to rid themselves of Thaddeus' balloon at any cost. First they had used their best marksmen within their own lines, but the range was too far. Light artillery also failed to find the balloon. So, during the very period when Thaddeus was away setting up the other balloon camp, they had sent out thirty-five sharpshooters in advance of their lines, each with the mission of shooting down the balloon.

When that failed too, they had sent five volunteers as spies into the Union camp itself. For the man who could destroy the balloon, a reward of one thousand dollars in gold and a commission as second lieutenant was offered. The "peddler" had been one of these spies. He and one other member of the group had finally given up and returned to Yorktown. The others had been captured.

Though he could only guess at the truth, Thaddeus still had plenty of evidence to convince him the Confederates were bent on his destruction. Security was tightened all through the balloon camp. Guards were strengthened. In conferences with his men, Thaddeus made sure that no suspicious character would ever be allowed near the balloon again.

Meanwhile the work of preparing the big guns for a siege

of Yorktown began in earnest, and the balloon ascensions continued day after day.

At first, after Fitz-John Porter's mishap, General McClellan snapped that none of his generals would ever be allowed to go up again in what he called "the confounded balloon." But he didn't mean it. Only two days later, Thaddeus got orders to take up General John Barnard, the army's chief of engineers. And before the month was out, General Porter himself had ventured aloft once more.

Between his long vigils in the air, Thaddeus found time for a thousand jobs on the ground. Some he could turn over to his father, who had become one of his chief ground assistants. During the long months of service on the Potomac, Clovis Lowe had become an expert in the balloon organization.

Other matters could be handled only by Thaddeus himself. He talked with D. D. Lathrop, a telegraph operator assigned to headquarters, about rigging wires so the balloon could send telegrams from the air. He kept constant check on the balloon at Warwick Court House, now being operated by James Allen and Eben Seaver. He wrestled with problems of supply and equipment, dashed off directions for work at balloon headquarters back in Washington, and worried night after night over the troubles of James Starkweather at Port Royal, South Carolina, and John Steiner at Cairo, Illinois.

Both his distant aeronauts had been vastly discouraged, and with reason. The commanding generals where they were located had shown no interest in balloons.

Starkweather had reached Port Royal on January 3, but it had been more than three months before he could get orders to ascend. Now he had at last got into action. The balloon *Washington* was making observations from the steamer *Mayflower* on the Savannah River, and Starkweather was happier than he had been in months.

Steiner, though, was in misery. The earnest little Dutchman knew little of spelling, and his letters showed it, but his anger at the way he was being treated in the West came through clearly.

He had reached Cairo on February 25 and found it impossible to get either General John Pope or General Henry Halleck to talk to him. No one would help. He couldn't get orders to go into action, he couldn't get equipment for his balloon, he couldn't even draw his pay.

By now he had been in the West nearly two months, and during that whole time he had seen service less than two weeks. And even this had been no thanks to Generals Pope or Halleck.

About the middle of March, Commodore Andrew Foote of the Navy had anchored his gunboats and mortar boats in the Mississippi River above Island 10 and begun a bombardment of that Confederate position. When John Steiner sought him out and offered his services, Foote accepted them gladly. The *Eagle* made ascensions from a flatboat, and officers from the mortar division went up to observe the effects of their fire on the enemy.

The observations were a great success. The observers discovered what they could not see from the ground—they were overshooting their targets. Corrections were made, and the Rebels were driven from their batteries.

But since the surrender of Island 10 in early April, Steiner reported, he had found no one willing to use his services.

"The officers hear are as dum as a set of asses," he stormed in one letter to Thaddeus.

"I am here like a dog wisout a tail," he wrote in another, "and I dond know ware I will be abel to draw my pay."

The Army of the Potomac buzzed with rumors of action as April, 1862, drew to a close. President Lincoln had agreed to send McClellan a part of McDowell's First Corps after all, and on April 22 General Franklin's division arrived. McClellan held them ready to make a dash up the York River when Yorktown fell.

And the defenses of Yorktown would be tested any day now. Almost all the big guns of the Army of the Potomac were in position for the shelling by the beginning of May. After the long preparations, the entire camp was electric with excitement.

The Rebel earthwork nearest to Thaddeus' balloon camp was a huge parapet of red clay known to the Union soldiers as the Red Fort. The gunners in the Red Fort had long ago picked Thaddeus as their favorite target, and every time he ascended they blazed away at him fiercely. But on May 2 they outdid themselves.

As the balloon rose that day, one of the heaviest cannonadings Thaddeus had ever heard began. Shots whizzed past, tearing big branches from the trees behind him. Explosions sent showers of dirt and debris into the air. Sharpshooters with rifles took up the deadly target practice, and Thaddeus winced as one minié ball came so close it set the basket ropes vibrating.

In the lulls, he could hear Union soldiers below him shouting to one another.

"They'll get him sure!"

"Why doesn't he come down?"

"If the balloon is hit, that's the end of Lowe!"

Thaddeus grinned. Already, he knew, he was rising above the range of the rifles. The bigger guns could not be elevated high enough to reach him. Peril was a part of his daily life by now. He knew when to be wary and when to relax. He let out a deep breath of relief.

BOOOOOOM!

It was a colossal explosion. It shook the very air about him and almost threw him to the floor of the basket.

What in the world could have happened?

Cautiously he looked over the side toward the Red Fort.

The air directly above it was full of dust, smoke, and great pieces of debris. Men were sprawled around one of the big Armstrong guns—and the gun itself was broken in two. Thaddeus stared at it for a long time before he realized what had happened. . . .

Fitz-John Porter was waiting for him when he came down, still a little shaken, half an hour later.

"For heaven's sake, Professor, what happened?"

Thaddeus' eyes twinkled. "You remember when you were captured by a shelter tent, sir? Well, in a manner of speaking, somebody broke a gun over my head. The gunners elevated it too high, trying to get my range, and when they fired, it exploded. I think the balloon should be credited with knocking out the biggest gun in the Red Fort."

The next day General McClellan completed his preparations for the great assault. Word went out that the battle would begin the following dawn. Thaddeus was ordered to make last-minute ascents at both ends of the Union line.

He hastened to Warwick, went up at noon, surveyed the entire left side of the Peninsula, and came down to make his report to General Keyes about four o'clock. Then he galloped back to the balloon camp opposite Yorktown.

Little Mac and the entire headquarters staff gathered for what they confidently believed would be the final ascent before the battle. As Thaddeus stepped into the basket, Fitz-John Porter strode toward him.

"I'm going with you, Professor."

Slowly the balloon began to rise. Then, in an instant, bedlam erupted.

BOOM! BOOM! CRACK! BOOM!

Every enemy battery on the Yorktown end of the line had opened up at the same time, as if the balloon's appearance had been a signal. Everywhere the air was filled with bursting shell and shot. The noise was deafening.

WHOOSH! ZINNNNNG! A shot passed directly through the cordage connecting the car with the balloon.

Thaddeus looked at General Porter. "Shall we go on?" he shouted.

Porter nodded almost absent-mindedly and began studying the ground directly below them.

On upward the balloon rose. The bombardment increased in intensity every second.

"Look!" It was Fitz-John Porter. Seizing Thaddeus' arm, he pointed below. Dust was rising from the ground where a shell had struck near General McClellan.

"And there!"

Following the general's pointed finger, Thaddeus saw a tent collapsing a few hundred feet away from the assembled staff officers. Soldiers were running for cover.

Now Porter was shouting into his ear.

". . . *have to go down! We're drawing fire to the whole area!*"

Thaddeus nodded and leaned out of the basket to give the signal to descend. The general was right. Troops were massed so thickly below them that the enemy's bombardment of the balloon could mean death to scores of men on the ground.

When they landed, Thaddeus saw General George Stoneman, the army's cavalry commander, talking hotly with McClellan.

". . . what this is doing to my horses, General! They have nearly stampeded. This balloon will be the death of them!"

McClellan turned to Thaddeus with a broad smile.

"You and Mr. Fitz always seem to be causing trouble by risking your lives, Professor. Now, in order to protect General Stoneman's horses and . . . ah . . . the lives of my men, perhaps you had better not make any more ascensions from this spot. Matter of fact, there should be no need for any more, eh Porter?"

"Right, sir!"

Thaddeus turned away smiling.

General Sam Heintzelman, Porter's corps commander, sent for Thaddeus shortly after dusk. The stern old general, a veteran of the Mexican War, ran his hand through his full beard and put his question bluntly.

"Professor, why did the Rebs make such a great effort to destroy your balloon yesterday and today?"

"I am not sure, sir. You think perhaps . . . ?"

Heintzelman grunted. "I don't know what to think. But there are rumors. Some say Joe Johnston has decided to evacuate Yorktown without a fight. Did you see any indications of it?"

"Why, no sir. It appeared to—"

Thaddeus never finished his sentence. At that instant, with a terrific crash, a twelve-inch shell landed a few feet away, directly on General Heintzelman's telegraph tent. Mud spattered both men from head to foot.

The general's long, thin hair waved wildly as he leapt from his camp stool and ran for the telegraph tent.

"It didn't explode—but it was enough to kill young Lathrop anyhow. Help me look, Professor."

They were pulling at the tattered remains of the tent when an agonized voice sounded behind them.

"My tent! My beautiful tent! And all my instruments!"

Heintzelman wheeled. "Lathrop! I thought you were inside."

"No, sir. I have been delivering a dispatch. But look at the mess they made!" The telegraph operator was almost in tears. "It'll take me hours to clean it up."

"Then get busy." The general's voice was stern, but Thaddeus saw his shoulders shaking with silent laughter. Apparently it hadn't dawned on Lathrop what a close call he had had with death.

Thaddeus looked off into the darkness, and saw the low outline of the anchored balloon rising over the treetops.

"It's the balloon, sir. They're still firing at it. Shall I move it for the safety of your camp?"

Heintzelman snorted. "I can stand it if you can. Besides, I'm interested in what's going on. I may go up in that contraption myself before the night is over. And now, perhaps we should both get some rest while we can."

"Professor! Wake up! You're needed!"

It seemed only minutes since he had closed his eyes. Aching with fatigue, he pulled himself up and looked at the figure standing in the doorway of his tent.

"Oh, Captain Moses. What's up?"

"General Heintzelman sent me. He wants you to make a night ascension and find out what's happening over there. The cannonading has gone on all night—until just a few minutes ago. Now there's a bright light somewhere in the town. Looks like a big fire."

"He thinks they're pulling out?"

"Well, he'd like *you* to see what *you* think."

Within minutes Thaddeus was high over the camp. The area was quiet now, and there was an unfamiliar softness in the air. For a moment he forgot the war and imagined he was back in Cincinnati, going up for a flight to the coast. Then, as the angry glow in the distance outlined the fortifications of Yorktown, the dream faded.

After studying the light closely, he descended and reported to General Heintzelman's tent.

"I saw the fire, sir. It looks like one large building near the river. May even be a burning vessel."

"And the campfires?"

"There were none, sir. But that's customary this close to dawn."

"Hmmmm. Then you—"

D. D. Lathrop, the telegraph operator, came running from his damaged tent.

"A telegram from General Porter, sir."

Heintzelman read it and clapped Thaddeus on the shoulder.

"I'll take that ride with you now, Professor. Porter has just talked with a pair of Rebel deserters. They say the enemy is getting out of Yorktown."

Together they raced back the short distance to the balloon camp. The ground crew was ready and waiting. They had only to step into the car and give the signal.

The sky was growing lighter now. In a little while it would be dawn. Together the tall young aeronaut and the elderly general searched the landscape for a hint of the enemy's actions.

"You have more practice at this sort of thing than I do, Professor. But blast me if I can see any sign of life."

Thaddeus nodded soberly. The glow of the fire was fading as dawn approached, and over all Yorktown lay an eerie quietude, like that of a ghost town. Not a man could be seen.

"I believe you're . . . look, General! Below us, on the right. General Porter is sending out skirmishers."

"He's feeling for 'em. We'll know in a minute."

Thaddeus held his breath as he watched. Would a sudden burst of fire from Yorktown reveal that its defenders had simply been lying low, hoping to lure the Union troops into an exposed position?

But the ragged line of skirmishers continued to move. On up to one of the advance earthworks of the enemy it went, and not a shot was fired. No movement could be seen within the Rebel lines.

Suddenly Thaddeus knew it was true. The enemy was gone, gone on the very day McClellan had planned to open his tremendous bombardment. He turned quickly and began raking the distant horizon with his glass.

"Look, General! The rear guard!"

They could see it now. Barely a mile past Yorktown a thick line of men and wagons choked the road that led up the Peninsula toward Williamsburg.

A harsh noise, somewhere between a growl and a roar, rose in Heintzelman's throat.

"Get this balloon down quick, Professor. We'll have to move fast to catch 'em!"

As the Union army advanced into deserted Yorktown, Thaddeus watched from the air. It was a sight to remember. Up from below him floated the jingle of harness and the rattle of sabers as Stoneman's cavalry saddled, mounted, and galloped off in pursuit of the enemy. And, from the York River on his right to the farthest distance he could see on the left, the foot soldiers moved across the watery no man's land like surf advancing along a sandy beach, and washed into the town of Yorktown itself.

The great fortifications were being taken without loss of a man.

Directly below him he could see big reels of wire being unwound as the telegraph lines were extended toward the town. He could recognize Lathrop, climbing down a pole, and the memory of last night's wreckage of the telegraph tent returned to him.

He was recalling Lathrop's excited indignation and laughing quietly to himself when a strange sight froze him in perplexed disbelief.

The telegraph operator had stepped down from the pole, and then . . . what? Was he doing some idiotic dance in celebration? He seemed to have thrown himself upward. . . .

The sound of the explosion reached Thaddeus' ear a fraction of a second later, even as his brain was beginning to function, even as the sight of showering debris sickened him with the terrible knowledge of what had happened.

Lathrop had stepped on a land mine. The Union would count one casualty, after all, in the capture of Yorktown.

17

MOST SHOT-AT MAN

DUSK was falling as the little aircraft carrier rounded a bend in the river. In answer to a signal from above, the men pulled the balloon down and anchored it to the flat deck. Thaddeus thrust long legs over the side of the basket and sighed wearily.

"There's a house ahead, overlooking the river. I believe it's the one."

"And the railroad bridge, Professor?"

"It's there, all right. But smoking. Looks like the Rebels set it afire."

"What about General Stoneman?"

Thaddeus looked at the little cluster of his assistants—James Allen, Eben Seaver, Locke Mason, his own father and the rest—and tried to make his grin cheerful.

"No sign of him. Gentlemen, I'm beginning to think we got here ahead of the cavalry."

"Then *we* are the advance guard of the whole Army of the Potomac!"

At Clovis Lowe's startled words, the men joined in a nervous cheer. Thaddeus cheered with them, but his mind was working feverishly.

Had he got too far in front and exposed the whole Aeronautics Corps to capture by the enemy? And if he had, how had it happened? Quickly he reviewed the orders he had been given five days before.

One of General McClellan's aides had explained the whole plan to him only a few hours after Yorktown had been occupied by the Union army.

"Let me show you on this map, Professor. The Rebels are retreating up the Peninsula toward Richmond. Part of the army is right behind them."

Looking at the map, Thaddeus nodded. He could see the whole Peninsula stretched out before him, with the York River on the north and the James on the south.

"Now, we'd like to cut them off if possible. We can't use the James yet because the Confederate ironclad *Virginia* is guarding it. But we can go up the York to West Point, seize the terminal of the railroad from Richmond, and hit them on the flank. Got it?"

"Yes, sir. And the balloons?"

"The general wants you to load all your men and equipment on the balloon boat and go up to the head of the York. See where the Pamunkey River flows into it at West Point? Well, you enter the Pamunkey and go about fifteen miles upstream.

"The railroad crosses the river there. There's a big white house nearby. They call the place White House. It's going to be the army's new headquarters. General Stoneman and the cavalry will go up the Peninsula and occupy it. We want you to join him there as soon as you can."

Well, Thaddeus thought, they had told him to hurry, and he had. Yorktown had been taken on Sunday. All day Monday, while a bitter battle raged a few miles up the Peninsula at Williamsburg, Thaddeus had been assembling his men and equipment and loading them at the Yorktown docks. On Tuesday he had set out upstream in company with the fleet carrying Franklin's division. There had been another battle at West Point on Wednesday when the Union troops landed. And now, Friday, he was approaching the spot where he had been ordered to join the cavalry. . . .

But where was the cavalry?

"Landing ahead!"

They could see the smoldering railroad bridge now, and a large house overlooking the river. As the steam tug carried the balloon boat in to the landing, Thaddeus took a quick mental count of his forces.

Along with three balloons, gas generators and other equipment he had his own assistants, his ground crews, and a small detail of soldiers. About one hundred fifty men in all, armed with muskets. And in the woods surrounding the landing, how many Confederates might be waiting for them?

"Lieutenant!"

The young officer in charge of the detail joined him and they talked hurriedly. By the time the last man was ashore, Thaddeus was ready with his plan.

"Men, we may be going into a trap here, so keep a sharp lookout. The lieutenant is going to take some men and surround the house. We'll leave a party here at the landing. If the lieutenant doesn't find anything, the rest of you will go up to the house with me."

He took a deep breath.

"Ready? Let's go!"

And the Aeronautics Corps moved out to occupy the new headquarters of the Army of the Potomac.

They met no opposition, but signs of hasty withdrawal were all about them. They found the farm overseer and two house servants hiding in a clump of pines near the house. Indoors, Thaddeus came upon the remains of a dinner still on the dining room table.

"The family just left," the overseer told him when Thaddeus had him brought in for questioning. "This house belongs to Mrs. Robert E. Lee. It's the home of one of her sons. I hope you will treat it gently, sir. This is where George Washington courted Mrs. Martha Custis."

Thaddeus nodded. "Believe me, we don't plan to damage it in any way. Lieutenant, let's see what we need to do outdoors."

"Yes, Colonel." It was an honorary rank only, for Thaddeus was still a civilian. But his authority was recognized.

Together they spread out their little force as widely as possible, to give an impression of strength to any Confederate scouts who might be watching. Campfires were kept burning from the river up to the house itself.

The night passed quietly. Next morning Thaddeus was anxiously scanning the landscape with his glasses when he saw a long column of troops approaching on horseback. He watched them for a while, gave a shout of triumph, and ran to meet them. In a few minutes he was greeting General George Stoneman.

The general stared at him in surprise.

"Professor Lowe! I thought . . . well, never mind. I'm glad to see you."

"General," Thaddeus said fervently, "you're not half as glad as I am."

For a week and a half the muddy units of the Army of the Potomac poured into the area around White House while McClellan and his generals planned the next step in the advance on Richmond.

Hundreds of men had fallen sick during the advance, Thaddeus' own Sergeant Eaton among them, but for all that there was an air of happy confidence in the camp. Richmond would soon be captured and the war would be over!

While the railroad bridge was being rebuilt, and while

supplies were coming up the Pamunkey in a never-ending flood of boats and barges, the plans began to take shape.

News came that the Rebels had destroyed the ironclad *Virginia* to keep it from falling into Union hands. That left the James River open, and for a while there was talk of moving the army's base to the James. Then word came from Washington that President Lincoln had decided to send the rest of McDowell's First Corps to join in the attack.

This was great news, Thaddeus knew, because McClellan wanted more men to be sure of winning. But there was bad news with it. The reinforcements would be coming down from Fredericksburg, so McClellan must not move to the James. His orders said he must keep his base of supplies at White House, and extend the right flank of his army north of Richmond so McDowell would not be cut off in the march to join him.

General Stoneman, whose opinion of Thaddeus was higher now than it had been when he blamed the balloon for scaring his horses, explained what this meant.

"It will put us in a dangerous position, Professor. I want you to understand it because you'll be with me when we move forward. You see, the Chickahominy River lies between us and Richmond. To advance on the city, we must cross it. But to hold our base here, we must keep part of the army on this side of the river."

"So we'll be straddling a river?"

"Exactly. And what's to keep Joe Johnston from attacking one part of the army while the other's separated from it?"

Thaddeus nodded thoughtfully. "And there's no way out of it?"

"None. The orders from Washington are clear." Stoneman turned back to the map. "My scouts tell me the Rebs have torn down every bridge on the Chickahominy. You and I will help locate spots for new bridges to be built. McClellan plans to throw two corps across the river, hold two more on the

right north of Richmond, and keep another in reserve between them, ready to support either in case of attack."

That made five corps, not counting McDowell's. Thaddeus
smiled as he recalled the way McClellan had reorganized the
Army of the Potomac. Lincoln had named his corps commanders for him, and it was no secret that Little Mac thought
the best generals had been passed over. So now, before the
advance on Richmond, he had rearranged his troops to form
two new corps, with Fitz-John Porter and William Franklin
in command. And he would see to it, Thaddeus suspected,
that Porter was where the fighting was fiercest.

"Where does McClellan think Johnston will attack?"

Stoneman set a gnarled finger down on the map north of
Richmond.

"Somewhere around here. McClellan figures he'll wait
until our left is across the river. Then he'll hit the right before McDowell can arrive." Stoneman smiled grimly. "Porter
and Franklin will be waiting for him on the right. Well, Professor, get your equipment ready. We move to the Chickahominy tomorrow."

The mighty army moved forward, with the cavalry and the
Aeronautics Corps in the advance. When they reached the
river, Thaddeus and General Stoneman made a balloon
ascent together and found they could see Richmond clearly
in the distance.

In the busy time that followed, the two of them became a
team for a while. They set up the beginnings of a headquarters camp in an area known as Gaines Hill and began making
regular ascents, noting good spots along the river for bridges
and watching closely for signs of the enemy.

Once, from a height of a thousand feet, they espied a Rebel
force concealed in the swampy land directly across the Chickahominy, and Stoneman had an idea.

"Didn't you experiment with aerial control of artillery fire while the army was on the Potomac?"

"Yes, General. Would you like to try it yourself?"

Stoneman's fierce eyes lit up. "Would I!"

They lowered the balloon. Stoneman shouted for an aide and ordered two batteries of artillery to be placed on a hill within view of the balloon.

"Watch me for your signals!"

Up went the balloon again. As the firing began, Thaddeus and the general could clearly see the Rebel position, though it was hidden from the gunners. Stoneman signaled corrections in range and elevation, the shells began crashing onto their target, and as the two men in the balloon watched, the enemy force beat a hasty retreat back toward Richmond.

Stoneman was delighted. "I've been ordered north of Richmond, around Mechanicsville," he said when they descended. "I'm asking that a balloon be sent there."

General McClellan had plans for the balloons, too. Thaddeus learned of them from General Andrew Humphreys, the army's chief topographical engineer. From now on, General Humphreys said, the three balloons with the army were too important to be left in the control of unit commanders. Thaddeus' orders would come directly from Little Mac's headquarters.

The balloon *Washington,* with a field generator, was taken to Mechanicsville. The *Constitution* was kept at Gaines Hill. That left the *Intrepid,* the biggest of the three, and for a while there was talk of sending it across the Chickahominy. In the end it was decided to keep it at Gaines Hill, too, and wire it for direct telegraph communication as soon as possible.

By now Keyes' corps had crossed the river, and most of Heintzelman's corps was across. New bridges were being thrown across the shallow stream at a dozen spots. Sumner, with the reserve corps, stayed near Gaines Mill, not far from

the headquarters camp. Porter and Franklin were far up at
the right end of the line, waiting for McDowell.

One day Thaddeus was preparing for an ascension from the
Gaines Hill camp when his father, who was serving as his
chief ground assistant, brought a young newspaper correspondent to him.

"Thaddeus, I believe you have met George Townsend of
the New York *Herald*."

"Indeed I have." Thaddeus tried to hide his grin. Everybody around headquarters knew about Townsend. He was
new with the army, but already he had gotten himself into
trouble. Not knowing about a strict rule that correspondents
must not ride out with advance parties, he had gone on a
reconnaissance a few days before, and had been put under
temporary arrest as a result. Somehow he had talked his way
back into the good graces of the top officers.

"Professor," the young reporter said, "I want to go up with
you on one of your ascensions."

"Why not now? We'll be ready in a few minutes."

"Great!" Townsend took a notebook from his pocket and
began observing the *Constitution* carefully. Gas was being fed
into the balloon from the generator. As the envelope swelled
out, its folds pulsed and shook as if they had a life of their
own.

"Looks like a big boa constrictor," the reporter said. He
wandered about the balloon camp making notes and disappeared from view. When Thaddeus went to look for him, he
found the *Herald* man sound asleep in one of the tents.

"Sorry," Townsend apologized. "On a job like this you
learn to sleep whenever you can."

"Maybe you can sleep in the basket."

Together they climbed in and Thaddeus gave the familiar
order.

"Stand by your cables!"

The twelve men in the ground crew payed out their ropes

slowly and the balloon glided gently upward. In a moment
the little Chickahominy lay below them. Then Richmond
itself appeared, the Capitol building of the Confederacy rising white and impressive on a hill in the distance. Rebel
troops could be seen everywhere.

"Hold hard and anchor fast!"

Thaddeus picked up his telescope. "Now, Mr. Townsend,
I have a sketch to make. Use the other glass if you like.'

For a while there was silence. Then the reporter spoke
nervously.

"Professor . . . that white puff of smoke, close below on the
edge of the timber. Do you suppose—"

BOOM!

"—they could be—"

RRAUWRR! The shrieking shell passed a few feet to their
left, and young Townsend's question suddenly became a statement of fact.

"—*shooting at us!*"

Thaddeus shook with laughter. He was accustomed to serving as an enemy target. Some of the soldiers had already begun calling him the most shot-at man in the whole army.

"Oh, it's nothing. You're perfectly safe up here."

BOOM! BOOM-BOOM!

Almost casually, Thaddeus laid down his notes.

"Haul in the cables!"

He looked at his companion. George Townsend's eyes were
shut and he seemed to be holding his breath.

WHOOOMP! A shell exploded so close the basket trem-
bled.

The *Constitution* came down rapidly. As the basket
touched ground, Clovis Lowe rushed forward.

"All right, Mr. Townsend," Thaddeus said briskly as he
climbed out. "Ride's over. Time to get out."

The reporter did not answer. Thaddeus was turning to see

what had happened when he heard a shout of laughter from his father.

"What's the matter? Did he fall asleep again?"

"No. Get some water quick, somebody. Mr. Townsend of the *Herald* has fainted!"

Now misfortune hit the Army of the Potomac a double blow. Word came from Washington that McDowell's marching orders had been suspended. He couldn't be spared at the moment, President Lincoln had decided. And, hard on the heels of this news, it began to rain.

Day after day, the rains continued. Gloom fell over the army's headquarters. The tiny Chickahominy suddenly became a muddy, roaring river, and the swamps on either side grew almost impassable.

"What happens now?" Thaddeus asked General Humphreys when he came to the balloon camp for an inspection. "Does the whole army cross the river?"

Humphreys gave an angry snort. "We can't. The order to hold White House is still in force. McDowell may be sent later—his orders were only suspended, not revoked. All we can do for the present is stay astraddle this confounded river and see what happens."

What happened was an ominous increase in activity on the enemy side. On May 27, Thaddeus was fired on by not one battery but three when he made an ascension. The barrage was so fierce he had to rise out of range and signal the balloon crew to tow him to another location before he came down.

Why were the Confederates suddenly so determined to shoot him down that they would direct the fire of three batteries at him?

Two days later he saw what may have been the answer. It left him cold with apprehension.

He had ascended in the morning at Gaines Hill and noted no change in the enemy positions. Then he had galloped up to Mechanicsville, six miles away, for an ascent in the *Washington*. The enemy was quite strong in that area. That was where the attack, if and when it came, was expected.

But, peering tensely through his glass, Thaddeus thought he noticed signs of fresh troops downstream, near the site of his earlier ascension. Was a quick new move under way?

He came down, got on his horse, and galloped back to Gaines Hill for a third ascent. By now it was sundown, but as the balloon rose higher his fears were confirmed.

The enemy was establishing a new camp near the area held by Keyes and Heintzelman on the far side of the river!

Looking at the swollen river below him, Thaddeus shivered. Had the Rebels learned that McDowell wasn't coming? And had they accordingly shifted their plan of attack from the Union right to the Union left?

If that was it, Keyes and Heintzelman were in for trouble. Unless reinforcements could reach them across the river, they would have to stand alone against the entire Rebel army.

And the Chickahominy was still rising.

"Haul in the cables!"

Before the balloon had reached the ground, he was dashing off his dispatch to General Humphreys:

". . . the enemy have this afternoon established another camp in front of this point. . . . They seem to be strengthening on our left. . . ."

The news sped to headquarters, and work on two new bridges was redoubled.

But, looking at the leaden skies above him, Thaddeus wondered if it would be in time.

On Friday, May 30, 1862, the skies opened and rain fell in sheets. Thunder volleyed like cannon. Lightning flashed wildly. Hour by hour the Chickahominy grew to a roaring flood, sweeping away bridges, overflowing the swamplands on each side.

Engineers worked valiantly to reinforce and complete the bridges that could take Sumner's corps across the river in case of a Rebel attack. But as fast as they got logs into place, the flood washed them away again.

On Saturday, Thaddeus left the camp at Gaines Hill and rode to Mechanicsville for an observation flight in the *Washington*. He was scarcely aloft before his worst fears were confirmed.

Columns of enemy soldiers and wagon trains were moving from Richmond toward Keyes' advance guard near the little crossroads known as Fair Oaks. . . .

The telegraph wire! That was what he needed—some way to communicate directly with McClellan's headquarters. But he had no telegraph at Mechanicsville.

He descended, dashed off a message, and sent it by courier to headquarters. Then he rose again for another anxious look.

The Rebel army was moving closer now to the Federal positions at Fair Oaks and Seven Pines. . . .

Now it was spreading out in line of battle. . . .

Thaddeus could stand it no longer. If he was to be of any real assistance, he must return to Gaines Hill. There he would be closer to the action, closer to headquarters, and closer to the telegraph wire.

At his signal, the ground crew hauled down the *Washington*. James Allen was waiting eagerly.

"Take it back up, James. I'm going to Gaines Hill."

He spurred his horse all the way, thinking desperately about the telegraph preparations he had begun the day before. Would Parker Spring, the operator, be waiting? Would the *Intrepid* have been inflated yet by the ground crew?

Clovis Lowe ran out to meet him as he reached the camp.

"Mr. Spring is here, son, and the telegraph wire is ready. But it will take an hour to finish inflating the *Intrepid*. Can you use the *Constitution*? It's ready to go."

Thaddeus flung his hat on the ground in frustration.

"I can use it, yes. But it's not big enough to carry Spring and the telegraph wire along with me. Rush the inflation of the *Intrepid* all you can, Father!"

While the work at the field generator went on, he made a quick ascent in the *Constitution.*

One look was enough. He groaned. The attack had already begun.

Frantically, he gave the signal to haul in the cables and sent another message to headquarters, reporting the position of the enemy forces. Then he looked helplessly at the big *Intrepid,* trying to will more gas into the envelope. It was maddening. The gas already in the *Constitution* was more than enough to finish filling the *Intrepid.* If there was only some way . . .

His eye fell on a big camp kettle lying on the ground, and an instant later he gave a roar that electrified the entire crew.

"The kettle! Quick, cut out the bottom!"

While a confused mechanic leapt to obey the order, Thaddeus sprinted toward the generator.

"Disconnect it! . . . bring the *Constitution* over here . . . hurry with that kettle!"

In minutes the desperate plan had worked. Using the bottomless kettle as a connecting joint, Thaddeus attached the bag of the *Constitution* to the *Intrepid.* Gas whooshed into the bigger envelope, and presto! The *Intrepid* was ready for use.

"The telegraph wire! Quick! . . . climb in, Mr. Spring . . . stand by your cables!"

Then they were high in the air, watching the conflict as it developed beneath them.

"Ready, Mr. Spring? Send this telegram. . . ."

While the Battle of Fair Oaks raged fiercely beneath him, Thaddeus sent a constant stream of reports to McClellan's headquarters. Remembering his warning two days before that the Rebels were shifting their forces, he felt numb with despair. Had the warning been too late?

It looked like it. The divided Army of the Potomac seemed doomed to a terrible defeat. Heintzelman and Keyes could not stand alone against the troops being flung against them. They were falling back, back toward the flooded river at their rear. . . .

Then he made out a great column advancing through the swamplands. Sumner's corps was crossing the Chickahominy.

A single bridge had been made strong enough to withstand the river's onslaughts. Over it poured the men who could turn the tide of the battle.

By night, when Thaddeus and his telegraph operator climbed stiffly out of the *Intrepid,* the crushing Confederate attack had been halted. And while he watched from the air the next morning, the Rebel forces began withdrawing toward Richmond.

Fair Oaks had been one of the great battles of the war, and disaster had been perilously close. An hour's slackening in the work on the Grapevine Bridge before the battle . . . a few minutes' delay in Sumner's advance . . . and the Union army might have been cut in two and destroyed.

Years later, when he was an old man, Thaddeus would read a verdict about that battle, written by General A. W. Greely:

"It may be safely claimed that the Union army was saved from destruction at the Battle of Fair Oaks . . . by the frequent and accurate reports of Lowe. . . ."

Three rainy, miserable weeks of waiting followed the battle. As Thaddeus watched Richmond constantly from his balloons, the Union army rebuilt the bridges across the Chickahominy, prepared once more for battle, and waited restlessly for the hoped-for arrival of McDowell's corps.

But, except for a single division, the reinforcements did not come. And every day more men fell ill. Thaddeus got a note from Locke Mason at White House with sad word from

Washington: Sergeant Eaton had died there of the fever he
had contracted on the Peninsula.

But Thaddeus scarcely had time to mourn his friend's
passing, for now another problem arose. Mason and Eben
Seaver refused to go on with their duties until they were paid.
Thaddeus knew the long delays in pay were bad on morale,
but the thought that they would quit their work during a
campaign was too much for him.

"Then you are no longer with the Aeronautics Corps," he
told them coldly. "Go back home and I'll send your pay
when it comes. We can get along without you."

Then, on June 25, word swept through the army that Mc-
Clellan was ready to attack.

The ground was dry enough to move the siege guns, the
bridges had been rebuilt, and Little Mac had decided to wait
for McDowell no longer. All his troops were now on the
Richmond side of the river except Fitz-John Porter's corps,
still guarding the right wing and the base of supplies at
White House.

A line of pickets was thrown forward toward Richmond.
Throughout the army, men prepared for action.

That night the picture suddenly changed again. Returning
crestfallen from a visit to headquarters, Thaddeus flung his
hat on a cot.

"There will be no attack," he told his father bitterly. "Mc-
Clellan has just learned that Stonewall Jackson is marching
from the Shenandoah to attack our right flank and rear."

He could see the danger all too well. Robert E. Lee, the
new Southern commander, had done just what McClellan
had feared. With Jackson approaching from the north, the
entire Union army was spread out like a long, thin sandwich
entering the hungry mouth of the South. Jackson was the
upper jaw, Lee the lower jaw. Together they could swallow
the entire army, bite by bite.

Clovis Lowe shook his head sadly. "White House."

"Exactly, father. That's been our weakness all the time. The order to hold White House as our base of supplies has kept our forces divided by the Chickahominy. Now the whole army is in danger again."

"What's the plan?"

"We're going to give up White House at last. We have to now. McClellan will try to move the base, and the army with it, to the James River. It's our only hope."

"Move the base in the face of an attack? Sounds dangerous to me."

"It is. But what can he do?"

Overnight the Army of the Potomac was on the defensive. The next day, while men worked frantically to load the supplies at White House on river boats, Porter fought a valiant rear-guard action against Rebel forces at Mechanicsville. Watching it from the Richmond side of the river, Thaddeus was able to report that the right wing held firm.

That night Porter's men moved their siege guns across the river but remained behind themselves, taking up a new position at Gaines Mill, not far from Thaddeus' old balloon camp at Gaines Hill. Here they would hold off the advancing enemy a little longer, if possible, while the rest of the army moved toward the James.

The next morning—Friday, June 27—the Battle of Gaines Mill began.

Thaddeus was up in his balloon early, but only by the greatest effort of will. He had worked too hard and slept too little. Now he too had fallen victim to the dreaded "Chickahominy fever." Chills swept his body. His face burned. But General Humphreys had called for ascents all through the day, and Thaddeus was grimly determined to make them himself.

All day he watched the terrible battle, reporting its progress to headquarters and wondering whether he would ever see Fitz-John Porter alive again. Once he was distracted by a strange sight—another balloon suddenly appeared in the air over Richmond. But he had little time to watch it, and when he looked again an hour later it was gone. It was the only Rebel balloon he saw during the entire war.

Late in the afternoon, as Porter's men began falling back toward the river, Thaddeus saw something that made him cold with fear. A large enemy column was pressing through the swamps, out of sight of the battle—heading directly toward the bridge Porter's forces were to cross to safety.

"Lower the balloon!"

By the time it had reached the ground, he had a dispatch ready for an orderly.

"Take this directly to General Humphreys or the chief of staff. It's urgent!"

Then, so weak from fever he could scarcely wave his arm, he gave the signal to be elevated again.

The sky was growing dark. Wearily he found the enemy column in his glass and watched it advancing toward the bridge. Then he scanned the right bank of the river. . . .

There!

Through the gloom he saw a body of fresh Union troops advancing at the double toward the threatened bridge. He sent up a feeble yell of triumph. His message had been in time.

But not until the reserves had fanned out around the bridge to protect it, not until Porter's dog-tired troops began struggling across it unopposed in the gathering darkness, did he give the signal to be lowered.

By the next day his fever was raging fiercely. Only a sense of triumph kept him on his feet. Porter had guarded White House until it was ready to be abandoned, and then had succeeded in withdrawing across the river. The move to the James was succeeding . . . and the balloon had helped to make it possible.

General Humphreys found Thaddeus working on one of his gas generators.

"Good heavens, man, you're white as a sheet! You should be in bed."

"Thank you, General, but I believe I can manage."

"Well, there's no need of it now. General McClellan wants all the balloon equipment packed up and moved to the new base ahead of the army. You have done great work, Professor, but from now on we'll be moving too rapidly for balloon observations to help. I want you to move back today—and when the rest of us get there, I want to find you in bed!"

It was Clovis Lowe who saw to the moving of the balloon corps to the new base on the James. Slumped on his horse, Thaddeus dozed feverishly through the trip.

He was conscious enough to give a weak cheer on July 2 when Clovis brought word to the hospital tent that the Army of the Potomac was safely at its new base. Then he relapsed into unconsciousness.

And, while the Army of the Potomac rested on the James from the Seven Days, Thaddeus was put on a boat with hundreds of other sick and wounded and sent home.

18

RED TAPE

GENERAL GEORGE McCLELLAN'S face still showed the strain of battle when Thaddeus was ushered into his headquarters near Antietam, Maryland, in late September of 1862. But his voice was as hearty as ever.

"Professor Lowe! I am glad to see you. You are completely recovered from the fever, then?"

"Thank you, sir, I am. And may I respectfully offer you my congratulations for driving General Lee's army out of Maryland?"

The general shut his eyes for a moment. "A terrible battle, Professor. Never have I seen such slaughter, and such valor. I wish you could have been here. A balloon would have been of great value to me."

"It was not my illness that prevented it, sir. It was army red tape. My transportation wagons had all been taken over by the Quartermaster Corps. No one would help me. It has taken me three days to arrive since you sent for me. As a civilian, I have no authority. . . ."

"I know." McClellan clenched a fist and let it fall softly on the table. "I have had my own difficulties with delays and red tape, believe me. Sometimes it seems hopeless. But in your own case, I hope we can arrange things better for the future."

"Yes, General?"

"You have more than proved your worth. I think the time is almost ripe for me to recommend that the Aeronautics Corps be made a distinct branch of the army, with you in command. How would you like a commission?"

Thaddeus' lean face flushed with pleasure. "General, it is all I have ever wished for. The corps could be a hundred times more effective as an independent command. My assistants and I simply cannot do our jobs properly as civilians."

McClellan smiled at his eagerness.

"Give me a little time then, Professor. I must wait until the atmosphere is right in Washington. Otherwise, my recommendation could do more harm than good. Meanwhile, welcome back to the army. It seems a long time since you were with us."

It did indeed seem a long time, Thaddeus told himself as he began setting up his balloon camp. More than two months had passed since he had been sent home from the Peninsula, and the war had taken many turns.

McClellan himself, the young aeronaut felt, had been badly treated during those two months—not by the enemy, but by Washington. From his new base on the James he had laid fresh plans to attack Richmond, but they had come to nothing. His critics said he was too slow and too timid. He wanted too many men, they insisted. So instead of getting the reinforcements he asked for, he was ordered back to Washington, practically in disgrace. The units of his army were handed over, piece by piece, to General John Pope, the new favorite at the capital.

McClellan had been forced to sit idle at Alexandria during the closing days of August while Pope led the Union forces to one of their greatest defeats, at the Second Battle of Bull Run. The routed army retreated in wild disorder to Washington. Fresh panic swept the North. Then, and only then, was McClellan returned to favor and asked to save the capital again.

Well, Thaddeus thought, he had done it . . . with the help of the soldiers who loved him so much. The Army of the Potomac had gone wild with joy when Little Mac was restored to command. In less than a week he had pulled the beaten fragments together, breathed new confidence into the men, and set off in pursuit of Robert E. Lee. And at Antietam, the bloodiest battle ever fought on American soil, he had halted the great Southern commander's invasion of the North.

President Lincoln had been waiting for just such a moment as McClellan had given him at Antietam. He announced that he would soon issue an Emancipation Proclamation, declaring that slaves throughout the Confederacy were free. Everyone at the capital had been delighted with Little Mac . . . for a day or so. But already Thaddeus had heard fresh complaints. While McClellan pleaded for shoes, food and equipment for his men, the critics were denouncing him for not moving into Virginia in hot pursuit of Lee.

Thaddeus told himself he was no military expert. Perhaps McClellan *was* slow to move. He only knew that, like the soldiers in the ranks, he felt a great affection and trust for the doughty little general.

Through the rest of September and October, while the army prepared for its advance into Virginia, Thaddeus and James Allen kept two balloons in the air almost constantly.

They were the only balloons in action now with the Union forces. James Starkweather's balloon had been damaged in a storm near Port Royal, and he had been sent home after about six months in the field. Worn out with the frustrations of his work in the South, he had resigned from the Aeronautics

Corps. John Steiner had finally come home from Cairo in disgust and talked of leaving the service himself.

For supervision of the ground work, Thaddeus relied more and more on his father. He had a handful of other assistants, but none of them was Clovis Lowe's equal. One of them, J. C. Freno—the same Freno who had once taken a balloon trip with him from Cincinnati—was doing such a poor job that Thaddeus hoped to find a replacement for him soon.

Meanwhile, the ascents continued. And late in October, McClellan was ready to advance.

The Army of the Potomac crossed into Virginia, marching once more in the direction of Richmond. Thaddeus was ordered to take all his equipment to Washington and prepare to join the army at a moment's notice when his services were needed.

He was putting a new coat of varnish on one of his balloons in the big Armory building a few days later when a Washington newspaper reporter he knew burst into the building.

"Professor, have you heard the news about McClellan?"

"What news?"

"He's been removed from command."

"*What?*"

"It's true." The reporter shook his head thoughtfully. "His enemies had their way at last. General Ambrose Burnside has been put in command. McClellan is out for good this time."

"I can't believe it."

"And that's not all. They've removed Fitz-John Porter too. There is talk that he will be blamed for Pope's defeat at Bull Run."

If Thaddeus was stunned by the news, its effect on the soldiers was even stronger. He heard hints of it in the reports that drifted back from Virginia during the next day or so. The men had threatened to revolt—to turn back, march on Washington itself, and overthrow the government that had removed their general. It was McClellan himself who had quieted them and persuaded them to accept their new commander. They must fight on for the Union, he told them. He would never forget them.

After his surprise had run its course, Thaddeus began to wonder whether he should give up his own efforts to serve his country. McClellan, who had understood and valued his work, was gone—and gone before he could establish the Aeronautics Corps as a separate command. Porter, the first general officer to sense what the balloons could do, was gone.

And the general in chief of all the Union armies was General Henry W. Halleck—that same officer, Thaddeus recalled bitterly, of whom John Steiner had written from Cairo:

"Gen. Hallack is no friend to the Aerontick Core."

Was it worth the effort to start all over again?

But if the soldiers in the army could fight on, who was he to give up and quit? No, he decided, his job was to go on as if nothing had happened. He would keep everything in readiness and wait for a call from General Burnside. Service to the Union was the important thing.

But the days passed and the call did not come.

The insiders at the capital said Burnside would fight Lee at Fredericksburg, Virginia. If that was the plan, Thaddeus told himself, the balloon would be needed. So when the army reached the Rappahannock River opposite Fredericksburg, he decided to wait for the call no longer. He sat down and wrote to the new commander, asking to be allowed to serve.

Four days later, on November 24, General Burnside sent for him. Thaddeus made the trip from the capital in a single day. On his arrival he was ordered to keep the balloon out of sight until the day of the attack, so the enemy would not know it was going to be used.

And so, on December 13, 1862, Thaddeus was in the air again, riding high over Burnside's headquarters to observe and report the Battle of Fredericksburg.

It was slaughter—sheer, sickening slaughter.

Busy taking up staff officers to see the progress of the fighting, Thaddeus could hardly bear to watch. And what was the need of watching? The balloon could be of no service in Burnside's kind of battle. His plan was simply to fling his divisions, one after another, against the Rebels' perfectly fortified positions in the heights beyond the town.

Soldiers advanced gallantly to certain death while their generals wept, but Burnside—a kindly, confused man who was badly out of his depth—only sent orders for more assaults.

By nightfall the Army of the Potomac was once again a broken and beaten force, and Thaddeus knew that before it moved again it would have yet another commander.

The change was more than a month in coming. And during those days, as Thaddeus kept his eye constantly on the victorious enemy across the Rappahannock, he began to feel more and more like an unwanted stepchild in the Army of the Potomac.

It was just as he had told General McClellan. Without a commission, he was all but helpless to fight the staggering red tape of the army.

His requests for supplies were shunted from one department to another. Payment for his men was constantly overdue. By the time he had trained a detail of soldiers for ground-crew duties, they were taken away from him and he had to start all over again.

It was true that the staff officers at headquarters relied heavily on his observations. But now there was no one at headquarters to help him with his problems. General Humphreys, the officer with whom he had worked so smoothly on the peninsula, had been given a command of his own.

To make matters worse, trouble arose over J. C. Freno.

The Philadelphian had never been a satisfactory assistant. When Thaddeus found an opportunity to hire James Allen's

brother Ezra, he discharged Freno—who promptly swore ven-
geance.

In a long letter to the army quartermaster's office, Freno
made outrageous accusations against his former chief. Thaddeus had cheated the government, he charged. He didn't work
at his job. He kept his father on the payroll when Clovis
Lowe's services were not needed.

Then, still wild with rage, Freno crept into the Armory at
Washington and deliberately sabotaged one of the balloons.

Thaddeus was busy drawing up papers calling for Freno's
arrest as a saboteur when a letter reached him from the quartermaster's office. His accounts, it said, would not be paid
until he had submitted answers in writing to charges made
against him by J. C. Freno.

For a moment his anger boiled over and he flung the letter
to the ground in fury. The idea that he should be ordered to
answer charges made against him by a man who had sabotaged
army equipment! And that he should answer, not to some
official court of inquiry, but to a captain in the Quartermaster
Corps!

At last, though, he swallowed his fury and did as he was
ordered. While James and Ezra Allen relieved him of balloon
work and Clovis wrestled with problems on the ground,
Thaddeus spent hours answering the charges point by point.

It was one way, he consoled himself, of seeing to it that his
accounts were paid.

General Joe Hooker was given command of the army on
January 25, 1863. Hooker had learned the value of balloons
early in the war, at Budd's Ferry on the Potomac, and Thaddeus was encouraged by the change. Now, perhaps, some of
the red tape and exasperations would be eliminated.

For a while it seemed his hopes would be realized. Hooker
was aggressively making plans for a fresh campaign against
Lee. He called for an increase in balloon activity. Thaddeus

got constant messages from General Butterfield, the chief of staff, asking for information.

Then a fresh irritation arose.

Some unknown critic of the Aeronautics Corps wrote a long letter to one of Hooker's aides, suggesting that Thaddeus' equipment was not practical. And even though every day in the field proved exactly the opposite, Thaddeus was directed to drop his work once more and write a lengthy answer.

Again, he did as he was told, and went on doggedly with his ascensions.

It was on April 7 that an order was issued from army head-quarters which, in the end, would wreck the Aeronautics Corps for good. It read as follows:

> Captain C. B. Comstock, Corps of Engineers, is assigned to the immediate charge of the Balloon establishment, and hereafter no issues or expenditures will be made on account of the same, except upon requisitions and accounts approved by that officer.

Thaddeus had taken young Cyrus Comstock up in the balloon several times of late. The memory of that young officer's attitude of cold-eyed authority still rankled in him.

"I don't like it," he told his father when Clovis Lowe brought him the order. "Trouble is brewing. I can feel it."

It came sooner than he expected. Four days later, Comstock sent a messenger with orders for Thaddeus to report to him at once.

Outwardly calm, Thaddeus reported. For a few minutes the young captain asked questions that indicated he had little idea of the problems the Aeronautics Corps had to face. Then he leaned back in his chair.

"I do not think the public interest requires the employ-ment of your father, Mr. Lowe."

It was like a slap in the face. Thaddeus felt his blood grow hot.

"You don't think *what*, Captain?"

Comstock's eyes met his briefly and then flicked away.

"You will notify him of that fact at once," he said. "And another thing—"

"Yes, *Captain?*" Thaddeus was holding himself in with an effort, but his emphasis on Comstock's junior rank was unmistakable.

"From now on, Mr. Lowe, all civilians connected with the balloons must observe these rules I have drawn up. And in the future, no one will be absent from duty without my permission."

Thaddeus stared at him. The man seemed to be deliberately setting out to infuriate everyone in the Aeronautics Corps—a little group of men who had repeatedly faced death without acclaim, without regular pay, without even the protection of a uniform if they were captured by the enemy.

The captain's voice was continuing.

". . . want you to prepare for me an inventory of all public property that has been under your charge. I will give you orders tomorrow affecting your own duties. And one more thing—"

"Well, Captain?"

"I think it will be necessary to reduce your pay from ten dollars a day to six."

How he managed to walk quietly away from Comstock without exploding, Thaddeus never knew.

The whole thing, he told himself, was simply beyond his understanding. A captain who knew nothing of balloons was taking over the entire corps, lock, stock and barrel—and going out of his way to humiliate Thaddeus in the process.

What else could he have intended? Clearly he was saying that Thaddeus had padded his payroll—and that he was not worth his own salt.

Remembering his struggles to build the corps into an air arm of which the Union could be proud, remembering the confidence placed in him by so many generals in the field, and remembering too the constant efforts to get enough money for his men to keep their families from starving, he simply couldn't believe it.

Somehow he found his way to his tent at the balloon camp. For a long time he sat at the little desk he and Clovis Lowe used to handle the business of the corps. Then he picked up a pen and addressed a letter to General Butterfield, Hooker's chief of staff.

As he wrote the details of his conversation with Captain Comstock and began to comment on it, the words poured out in a white-hot flow.

"At the breaking out of the rebellion I was urged to offer my services to the Government as an Aeronaut. I did so, at the sacrifice of my long cherished enterprises. . . .

"During my first operations . . . I used my own machinery and expended considerable private means and two months labor, for all of which I have never received pay. . . .

"I was offered $30 per day for each day I would keep one balloon inflated in the field. . . . I declined this offer and offered my services for $10 per day. . . .

"I have labored incessantly for the interest of the Government. . . . I have never shrunk from duty or danger. . . .

"I cannot honorably serve for the sum named by Capt. Comstock without first refunding to the Government the excess of that amount which I have been receiving ever since I have been in the service; this my very limited means will not allow, for it requires full the salary I have received to support myself in the field, and my family at home.

"Therefore, out of respect to myself and the duty I owe my family, it will be impossible for me to serve. . . ."

Looking at his own words, he could still scarcely believe it. He was leaving the army.

No, he told himself bitterly, he was not leaving. He was being driven out.

But could he leave on the very eve of Joe Hooker's first campaign? Putting aside his personal feelings, was it fair to the Army of the Potomac? Was it fair to his country?

Sighing, he picked up the pen again.

"Notwithstanding," he wrote, "as I have promised the Commanding General that nothing should be lacking on my part to render the greatest possible service during the next battle . . . I will offer my services until that time, free of charge to the Government."

19

THE LAST BATTLE

Even after he had sent off his letter, he could not believe he would really be leaving the service soon.

"Things will change," he told his father with more cheerfulness than he felt. "General Butterfield is a reasonable man. He knows we can't work under such conditions."

"What do you think will happen, then?"

"I think they'll take Comstock off our necks."

"And if they don't? Is your letter only a bluff?"

Thaddeus shook his head slowly. "No, sir. It is no bluff."

Once more, the army red tape took over. His letter addressed to General Butterfield was promptly sent back to him by a headquarters aide. Since it had to do with balloons, it must be "forwarded through the proper channel."

That meant Comstock.

Thaddeus turned the letter over to the captain. Two days later it was returned to him with a terse note from another staff officer pointing out simply that Captain Comstock was in charge of balloons.

There was no indication on the letter that General Butterfield had ever seen it.

Then that was that, Thaddeus told himself. There was nothing left to do but quit. First, though, he would do what he had promised. He would serve free of charge in the battle about to be fought.

Clovis Lowe told him goodbye and left for home, and Thaddeus returned to his work. There was much to do. Observation flights must be made, equipment must be sent back to Washington for repairs, plans must be worked out for moving the balloons in the coming campaign.

At every step, it seemed, he ran into difficulties with Cyrus Comstock.

The captain seemed to take a pleasure in finding fault. When he learned that Thaddeus had written to the Secretary of War, offering to provide a balloon for the Union troops near Baton Rouge, Louisiana, he was indignant.

"Why did you do this without my authority?"

Thaddeus looked at him in surprise.

"Captain, I have had frequent communication with the Secretary of War in the past. Remember that I am a civilian. No one has ever objected before now. I am only trying to put my equipment and ability at the service of my country."

But, as usual, Comstock had the last word. When the Secretary of War asked for a balloon and aeronaut to be sent to the troops in the South as soon as possible, the captain blocked the whole plan. He could not spare an aeronaut, he said.

Thaddeus offered to go himself. Comstock refused, and there the matter ended. The troops near Baton Rouge never got their balloon.

But now more immediate events were afoot. General Joe Hooker had worked out his plan for destroying Robert E. Lee's army at Fredericksburg. The Army of the Potomac was ready to move.

The plan sounded to Thaddeus like a good one. Hooker would leave part of his army across the river from the town, to threaten Lee from the front. Then he would march the other units in a wide circle to the west, cross the Rappahannock, and fall on Lee's left flank and rear from the direction of Chancellorsville.

Balloon observations, the general made clear, would be urgently important. Both balloons now in the field must be kept up constantly. Telegraph communication would be arranged whenever possible. And any person, regardless of rank, who was caught tampering with the balloons' telegraph wires would be shot.

Now that the time had come, Thaddeus observed, Cyrus Comstock was sent off on other tasks and Thaddeus was left to handle the work himself. In a way it was a relief. At last he could do his work without interference.

By Tuesday, April 28, troops were moving out of camp for the encircling movement. It was a windy day, too windy for the balloons, but Thaddeus went up anyhow, again and again, to watch for any sign of a change in the enemy's position.

The pace quickened on Wednesday. Thaddeus worked all day and night. Toward the end of the day, after a series of ascents, he was ordered to move the *Eagle* upstream to Bank's Ford and to hold the *Washington* ready to cross the Rappahannock. He called the Allen brothers in for a conference.

"James, I want you to stay with the *Washington*. You'd better prepare rations in case you have to move by daybreak. Ezra, you take the *Eagle* to the ford. But first we need a final inspection of the Rebel camps. Feel like a nighttime ride?"

"Yes, sir!"

"Very well. You will be towed along the river bank after dark." Thaddeus ran a hand through his hair. "We've got a lot of work ahead of us, boys. Let's show them what the Aeronautics Corps can do!"

He spent the rest of the night shuttling back and forth between the two balloons, checking with his assistant aeronauts, arranging telegraph hookups. Early morning found him with Ezra Allen at Bank's Ford, fighting the winds that

made an ascent all but impossible. By midmorning he was
reporting from the air on the strength of enemy outposts
along the river. In the afternoon he went back downstream
to make observations from the *Washington.*

That night he dashed off more orders to his assistants, conferred with aides of General Sedgwick, the officer in command
of the troops opposite Fredericksburg, and fell onto a cot at
last for a few hours' restless sleep.

He was up early the next morning, reporting ominous
movements of large enemy columns advancing upriver. Lee
had got wind of Hooker's move, it appeared, and was sending
out troops to meet him!

Four times during the morning he reported Rebel columns
moving in the direction of Chancellorsville. Then, about
noon, he heard the great thundering of guns.

"In a west northwest direction about twelve miles," he
messaged, "an engagement is going on. . . ."

The Battle of Chancellorsville had begun.

All through that afternoon Thaddeus rode the winds over
the Rappahannock, reporting enemy movements at the scene
of the battle and back in the area of Fredericksburg as well.
When he came down for a few hours' rest at nightfall, he
found puzzled looks on the faces of the officers at General
Sedgwick's headquarters.

"I can't understand what General Hooker is doing," he
heard a colonel mutter. "Everything was going according to
plan, and then he pulled back. Why?"

Thaddeus was too weary to ask questions. A few winks of
sleep and he was back at the balloon camp, ready to ascend
with the first hint of dawn.

By Saturday afternoon he was moving like a man in a
dream. His body had never recovered from its long bout with
Chickahominy fever, and four days and nights of almost constant work had left their mark on him. Doggedly he went on
filing his reports, answering urgent questions flashed to him

by General Butterfield, straining his eyes for every movement that might be of importance.

Ezra Allen was reporting regularly from Bank's Ford, and the messages from the two balloons indicated something strange was afoot.

The enemy was not building up troops where he was expected to. Columns were moving along the Plank Road in a direction that would not take them to the scene of the fighting. What was happening?

Not until sundown did the Army of the Potomac learn what was going on. Far off, out of range of Thaddeus' glass, General Stonewall Jackson had swung his Rebel troops around the whole front of the Union line. And about dusk, as the men on Joe Hooker's unguarded right flank prepared to eat, the Southern forces fell on them with wild whoops and a shattering volley of shots.

Thaddeus could not know it as he listened anxiously to the distant booming of the guns, but the Battle of Chancellorsville was all but lost.

On Sunday the size of the disaster became clear.

Union troops had crossed the river at Fredericksburg, timing their movements with those of Joe Hooker on the far right of the line. The plan had been for these men of Sedgwick's to unite with Hooker and finish off the enemy. But by noon the entire army was falling back on the river, looking for places to cross without being destroyed.

Thaddeus got fresh orders: watch with extra care for strong and weak points on the south side of the river.

So again, and now for the fifth day in a row, he clung to the ropes of the balloon car and hoarsely dictated messages to his telegraph operator.

"The enemy are advancing in large force to attack our forces on the right of Fredericksburg. . . ."

"The enemy are engaged in full force, and driving our forces badly. . . ."

"The enemy have driven our left with a large force and have possession of the river opposite Falmouth. . . ."

Thaddeus felt an overwhelming sense of despair. The Army of the Potomac had been defeated again. Twice in five months, the men George McClellan had molded into the greatest army on the continent had been led into disaster.

Two days later he sought out Captain Cyrus Comstock.

"Captain, there are repairs that must be made on the balloons. It is a delicate job. I would suggest . . ."

"Thank you, Mr. Lowe. I will select someone to repair the balloons."

Thaddeus no longer was able to feel anger.

"Very well, Captain. I only hope it will be as simple as you think. And now that the battle is over, I would like to be relieved of duty as soon as it is convenient. James and Ezra Allen can take over my work—under your orders, of course. I am sick. I have served without pay for a month."

"If you are going, Mr. Lowe, we can probably spare you better now than at any other time."

Thaddeus nodded and turned away.

On May 7, 1863, an aide from General Hooker's headquarters dashed into the balloon camp of the Army of the Potomac.

"Where is Professor Lowe? The general wants him to make an ascension at once."

A man looked up from his work on a generator.

"Professor Lowe? Why, he's not with the army any more. Didn't you know?"

"Good heavens, no." And the aide hastened back to inform the commanding general of the army that, without his knowledge, the services of the father of the Aeronautics Corps had been dispensed with.

20

NEW WORLDS

As THE great crowd surged closer, one of the men working on the balloon rose to his feet, cupped his hands to his mouth, and let out a shout.

"Stand back, please. *Stand back!* You'll damage the balloon!"

A light-hearted cheer answered him, and the cry passed back through the thousands of New Yorkers gathered in Central Park.

"Stand back!"

"Make way for the bride and groom!"

A reporter elbowed through the throng. "Where's Professor Lowe?"

"Be patient. He'll be here soon."

As the reporter stared out at the crowd, an expression of awe came over his face.

"There must be twenty-five thousand people here! Let's hope the Professor doesn't disappoint them. Will Dr. Henry Ward Beecher really show up for the wedding?"

"Look, mister, you know as much about it as I do."

It was November 8, 1865, and the assembled New Yorkers were ready to enjoy a new thrill, the sight of a wedding in the clouds. John F. Boynton of Syracuse, New York, and Miss Mary West Jenkins of St. Louis would be the bride and groom. Dr. Beecher, the famous minister, had been asked to perform the ceremony.

"Well, it's a great day for a—"

Far out on the edge of the crowd a low roar sounded. It mounted to a mighty cry of welcome as a little group of people appeared in the distance.

"Here comes the bride!"

"Hooray for the wedding!"

Professor Thaddeus S. C. Lowe, tall and handsome in a new suit and high silk hat, led the procession, bowing and waving as he walked. Behind him came the young couple, followed by the rest of the wedding party. The crowd parted to let them through, and they walked quickly toward the big balloon.

"The preacher! Where's the preacher?"

Thaddeus exchanged glances with the bride and groom, and smiled wryly. He reached the balloon, found a large box, and climbed onto it. As he looked out over the crowd, the shouts and laughter died away.

"Ladies and gentlemen!"

"Hooray for Professor Lowe!"

"Please! Please! I have an announcement to make. As you know, Dr. Henry Ward Beecher was asked to perform this wedding in midair . . ."

"Hooray for Doctor Beecher!"

". . . but he has declined."

The cry of disappointment rose in a great "Ohhhh!" Thaddeus raised his hands for silence.

"The good doctor wants to go to heaven—but not in a balloon!"

Laughter, shouts and hand-clapping greeted his words. For

a moment the crowd had looked angry, but now it was good-humored again. Thaddeus lifted his voice once more.

"The wedding has just been performed, at the Fifth Avenue Hotel—*Wait! Wait!*—but the ascension will take place as scheduled. The bride and groom will take their *honeymoon trip* in the balloon!"

Now the crowd was shouting louder than ever.

"Hooray for the honeymooners!"

"Hooray for the balloon!"

Then another cry was raised. It swept across the park until it seemed everyone was shouting the same question.

"Alone, Professor? Alone?"

Thaddeus broke into a laugh.

"No! I'm going with them!"

After that it was bedlam. Somehow the bride and groom were helped into the beautifully decorated balloon basket. One of the bridesmaids, blushing prettily, followed them. Thaddeus thrust one long leg into the basket and turned once again to the crowd.

"What better way to start a marriage than up in the clouds?"

Only a few heard him, but it didn't matter. The cheers rose in volley after volley as the balloon was released from its ground ropes and sailed majestically up into the air.

Inside the basket, the bride and groom were breathless with excitement, and the little bridesmaid was watching the earth in frightened fascination. Thaddeus turned to John Boynton with a smile.

"Well! Now that there is time to talk, let me wish you both a long and happy union. May all your journeys be as pleasant as this one."

"Thank you, Professor. And may all your balloon ascensions be as successful."

Thaddeus smiled at the couple again, but there was a look of regret in his eyes.

"I didn't tell you, did I? This is my last ascension. I'm giving up ballooning for good."

And high time, he told himself as the balloon sailed grandly over the New York countryside with its happy passengers. He was thirty-three years old now. If he was going to change his career, then the sooner the better.

He had been forced to it. No one seemed able to see, as he could, how important air travel could become—just as Washington had been unable to see the need for continuing the Aeronautics Corps during the war.

He had tried. After the Battle of Chancellorsville he had returned to Washington, submitted a long report to the Secretary of War, and worked week after week to persuade the authorities that aeronauts—not civilians, but uniformed military aeronauts—were urgently needed in the Union armies.

But it was no use. The recommendations, along with warm letters of support from many of the generals under whom he had served, were ignored.

James and Ezra Allen tried to keep the corps in operation, but matters went from bad to worse. When General Lee invaded the North again in June and the Army of the Potomac set out in pursuit, the balloon train was ordered back to Washington and the corps was disbanded. In the bloody battle of Gettysburg, the Union had no aerial observation.

Still weak from his bouts with the fever, Thaddeus had at last taken his doctor's advice and left the capital. He bought a farm near George Washington's old headquarters at Valley Forge, and settled down to rest and get acquainted with his family.

General U. S. Grant took command of the Union armies in 1864, and as the war rocked on, Thaddeus began dreaming of building an airship that could control its own flight. He went to Philadelphia to talk to his old friends at the Franklin Institute about it. The institute published a paper of his, "The Air Navigable Without the Aid of Balloons," and for a while Thaddeus hoped he would get enough support to build a real airship.

But, though he tried for more than a year, he couldn't find the money for the work. People weren't interested.

The war ended in April, 1865. President Lincoln was assassinated a few days later, and the country was plunged into the bitterness of Reconstruction. No one had the time or interest to encourage a scientist with a dream of powered flight—a scientist with a wife and family to support.

Then he would turn to other things. During the long days of rest and recuperation on the farm, he had worked out a plan for an ice-making machine. America knew nothing of refrigeration, but it would be glad to learn. This was no dream for the future, like air travel—this was something for the present.

So after the honeymoon flight, Thaddeus put his inventive genius to work in other fields. He traveled throughout the country, installing ice-making machinery in towns that had never had artificial ice before. He experimented with cold storage. He invented a new process for producing gas for heat and illumination.

As the years passed, he grew wealthy and famous. He moved to a fine town house in Norristown, Pennsylvania, where he received honors from all over the nation—not for his work with balloons, but for bringing cheap refrigeration, light and heat to thousands of his fellow countrymen.

In 1885 the Franklin Institute awarded him its highest honor, the Elliott Cresson Medal for services to mankind.

Three years later he moved to Pasadena, California, and began a new adventure. If he could no longer look at the stars from a balloon, he would look at them through a telescope. He built an observatory on top of a mountain named Mount Lowe in his honor. Then he built a railroad up the mountain to carry people to it.

As the years ran on, he was constantly working, dreaming,

planning new inventions. In 1897 he developed a new coke oven system and added more fame to his name. The next year, during the Spanish American War, he offered his services to the government for a new idea—the building of an underwater ship to fight the enemy fleet. But no one took the idea of submarines seriously.

The arrival of the twentieth century found Thaddeus Lowe still happily at work. He and Leontine had had ten children, and now there were grandchildren back in Pennsylvania as well as in California. The proud grandparents took frequent trips back east.

They had great times in the reunions at the big house in Norristown, which was still in the family. Thaddeus would hire carriages and take the children on trips to Valley Forge, or make fireworks for them, or put on great shows with toy balloons. They were a little afraid of this tall, intense grandfather of theirs, but they worshiped him.

Once he took a trip back to Jefferson Mills, New Hampshire. His old hometown had changed its name to Riverton, but it had not forgotten its most famous citizen. On Thaddeus' seventy-fifth birthday a celebration was held for him and the Lowe Memorial Union Chapel was dedicated in his honor.

As he grew still older, America at last began to realize the importance of air flight. Airplanes became a reality, and Thaddeus fell to dreaming again. It was not too late, even yet! He would still cross the ocean. He would build a great "Planet Airship" and sail it all around the world!

But perhaps he knew that, this time, it truly was only a dream. For he was growing feeble now, feeble in body if not in mind. He toyed with the airship idea for a while, then sighed and sat down to write his recollections of the far-off days when he was chief aeronaut of the Army of the Potomac, the most shot-at man in the Civil War.

He was still working on them, and still dreaming of the

great future in the air, when he died on January 16, 1913, at the age of eighty.

The *Scientific American,* which had once smiled at his idea of crossing the ocean by air, noted his passing with deep respect.

"He was a type of brilliant all-around inventor and engineer that is fast disappearing," its editorial said. It praised him chiefly for his work with water gas, refrigeration, metallurgical furnaces and coke ovens, and mentioned his balloon work only in passing—for already America had become more interested in airplanes than in balloons.

But half a century later Thaddeus Lowe's work with balloons was still serving America. Aerostats were coming into their own at last.

Balloons were carrying men upward for observations that could not be made in other craft. Unmanned balloons went higher. Following in the steps that he had helped to pioneer, a new breed of dreamers were riding the air to the very edge of outer space.

There are some today who say the world is too advanced for old-time adventure. Everything is too complicated now, they insist. There is no room for one person to dream of great deeds.

But it is doubtful if the mountain boy from New Hampshire, looking upward toward mysteries still unsolved in the skies, would agree.

BIBLIOGRAPHY

THADDEUS LOWE'S own story of his life, *My Balloons in Peace and War,* was the chief unpublished source for this book. There were many more, among them a long memoir generously written for the author by Russell J. Brownback, Professor Lowe's grandson, about his grandparents; letters from Mrs. Grace Stanley Plaisted of Jefferson, N. H., whose grandmother knew the Lowe family; documents at the Franklin Institute in Philadelphia and the General Services Administration in Washington; and a vast collection of letters, orders, reports and the like in the Lowe Papers at the Institute of the Aerospace Sciences in New York City.

The Lowe Papers also provided a wealth of newspaper and magazine accounts of his adventures, in addition to which—and with the assistance of librarians, researchers and historical society officials in various cities in the United States and Canada—other contemporary reports were found. Of especial value were articles in *Harper's Weekly, Scientific American,* the Hamilton (Canada) *Daily Spectator,* the New York *Times,* the Philadelphia *Inquirer,* and the five daily newspapers publishing in Cincinnati in 1861.

General reference works included the *Dictionary of American Biography; Appleton's Cyclopaedia of American Biography; Who Was Who in America* (Volume I, 1897-1942); the *Biographical Directory of the American Congress, 1774-1949; Compton's Pictured Encyclopedia;* and the *Encyclopaedia Britannica.*

The most important published work on Thaddeus Lowe's military service is a magnificent volume, *Aeronautics in the Union and Confederate Armies,* Volume I, by F. Stansbury Haydon (Johns Hopkins Press, 1941). Unhappily, a projected second volume was never published and the story is left incomplete.

The chief general source for the war years was that vast library published by the United States Government under the title, *The War of the Rebellion: A Compilation of the Official Records of the Union and Confederate Armies.* Its companion work, *Official Records of the Union and Confederate Navies,* was also helpful.

In addition, the following books and articles were consulted:

Abraham Lincoln: The War Years, Vol. I, by Carl Sandburg. Harcourt, Brace & Co., New York, 1939.

"Aeronautics in the Civil War," by J. D. Squires, in *American Historical Review,* July, 1937.

The American Iliad, by Otto Eisenschiml and Ralph Newman. Bobbs-Merrill, Indianapolis, 1947.

"Balloons in War," by Gen. A. W. Greely, in *Harper's Monthly,* June, 1900.

Battles and Leaders of the Civil War. Thomas Yoseloff, Inc., New York and London, 1887 and 1956.

The Civil War, a Narrative: Fort Sumter to Perryville, by Shelby Foote. Random House, New York, 1958.

The Civil War: A New One-Volume History, by Harry Hansen. New American Library, New York, 1961.

A Civil War Treasury of Tales, Legends and Folklore, edited by B. A. Botkin. Random House, New York, 1960.

Fiasco at Fredericksburg, by Vorin E. Whan, Jr. Pennsylvania State University Press, 1961.

Fighting Joe Hooker, by Walter H. Hebert. Bobbs-Merrill, Indianapolis and New York, 1944.

First Century of Flight in America, by Jeremiah Milbank. Princeton University Press, Princeton, 1943.

From Bull Run to Chancellorsville, by Newton M. Curtis. G. P. Putnam's Sons, New York and London, 1906.

From Manassas to Appomattox, by James Longstreet. Lippincott, Philadelpia, 1896.

General George B. McClellan, Shield of the Union, by Warren W. Hassler, Jr. Louisiana State University Press, Baton Rouge, 1957.

The Hidden Face of the Civil War, by Otto Eisenschiml. Bobbs-Merrill, Indianapolis and New York, 1961.

History of Coos County, New Hampshire. W. A. Fergusson & Co., Syracuse, N. Y., 1888.

A History of Flying, by Charles H. Gibbs-Smith. Fred A. Praeger, New York, 1954.

History of the Town of Jefferson, N.H., 1773-1927, by George C. Evans. Granite State Press, Manchester, N.H., 1927.

Lincoln and the Tools of War, by Robert V. Bruce. Bobbs-Merrill, Indianapolis and New York, 1956.

Lincoln in the Telegraph Office, by David Homer Bates. The Century Co., New York, 1907.

Lincoln Finds a General, by Kenneth P. Williams. Macmillan, New York, 1949.

The Lincoln Papers, Vol. II, by David C. Mearns. Doubleday & Co., Garden City, 1948.

The Photographic History of the Civil War, Francis Trevelyan Miller, ed. Review of Reviews Co., New York, 1911.

Randolph Old and New, by George Cross. Randolph, N.H., 1924.

The Rebellion Record: A Diary of American Events, edited by Frank Moore. G. P. Putnam's Sons, 1861-63, D. Van Nostrand, 1864-68, New York.

"Reminiscences of Ballooning in the Civil War," by W. J. Rhees, in *The Chautauquan,* June, 1898.

Reveille in Washington, by Margaret Leech. Harper & Brothers, New York and London, 1941.

A System of Aeronautics, by John Wise. J. A. Speel, Philadelphia, 1850.

The Story of the Confederacy, by Robert Selph Henry. Bobbs-Merrill, New York and Indianapolis, 1931.

Thaddeus Lowe: America's One-Man Air Corps, by Mary Hoehling. Julian Messner Inc., New York, 1958.

"Thaddeus S. C. Lowe: One of America's Greatest Inventive Geniuses and Benefactors," by George W. James, in *Arena,* October, 1907.

This Hallowed Ground, by Bruce Catton. Doubleday & Co., Garden City, 1956.

Through the Air, by John Wise. Today Printing & Publishing Co., Philadelphia, 1873.

Tragic Years, 1860-1865, Vol. I, by Paul M. Angle and Earl S. Miers. Simon and Schuster, New York, 1960.

The War for the Union, Vol. II, by Allan Nevins. Charles Scribner's Sons, New York, 1960.

Yankee Reporter on the Road to Richmond or Rustics in Rebellion, by George Alfred Townsend. University of North Carolina Press, Chapel Hill, 1950.

Yankee Reporters 1861-65, by Emmet Crozier. Oxford University Press, New York, 1956.

INDEX

The Author

LYDEL SIMS grew up in south Louisiana. A graduate of Northwest Louisiana State College, Mr. Sims completed two years of graduate work. Since 1949, he has been Page-One feature columnist on the *Commercial Appeal* of Memphis, Tennessee. He was the recipient of the National Headliners Award for the outstanding feature column. Having combined newspaper work with free-lance magazine writing, Mr. Sims has been a contributor to a wide variety of national magazines. He is the co-author of two books about World War II and the author of a biography of John Wesley for young people. Married and the father of two girls, Mr. Sims is a long-time Civil War buff and ardent fisherman.